Your letters...

Here are a few letters Phil's received about *Grange Hill*...

IT'S NOT DISGUSTING!

Grange Hill is an excellent programme and very much like the school I attend. My parents have nothing against the programme and I do not understand how some mothers can be disgusted by the behaviour and language of the *Grange Hill* cast.

I loved the first *Grange Hill Magazine* and thought it was very witty, interesting and amusing.

Amanda White, Middlesex.

HOURS OF FUN

I think *Grange Hill* is great. I've watched every single programme without fail and not one has been boring. *Grange Hill* has given me hours and hours of fun!

Richard Dinsdale, Devon.

GREAT MAG!

The *Grange Hill Magazine* was very good and well worth 50p. Absolutely everything was inside, including my favourite characters — Tucker, Benny and Trisha. I enjoyed reading the picture stories and hope there'll be many more issues in the future.

Kevin Humphreys, Bucks.

THE BEST AROUND!

Grange Hill is the best TV show that England and the BBC have ever sent to New Zealand. It is even better than *Dr. Who*, which is my second best show!

All the cast are fantastic — especially the girls.

Stephen Rhys Ewart, New Zealand.

GIVE TODD A CHANCE!

I really love *Grange Hill* and that's for one good reason — Todd Carty! Talk about gorgeous, he beats so-called hunks like Sting and Adam Ant by miles.

Why doesn't someone give Todd his own TV show? I'm sure it'd be brilliant!

Janine Smith, Grimsby.

CONTE[NTS]

P. 50 SATURDAY MORNING FEVER

P. 2 A letter from Phil Redmond
P. 3 Contents and Your Letters
P. 4 **The Tell-Tale Stamp —** terrific drawn story
P. 14 **Triple Trouble!** Can you imagine having a chaperone?
P. 16 **Please Miss, I Think I Love You!** Falling for a teacher can be very dangerous ...
P. 17 Pin-up of Duane
P. 18 Pin-up of Pamela

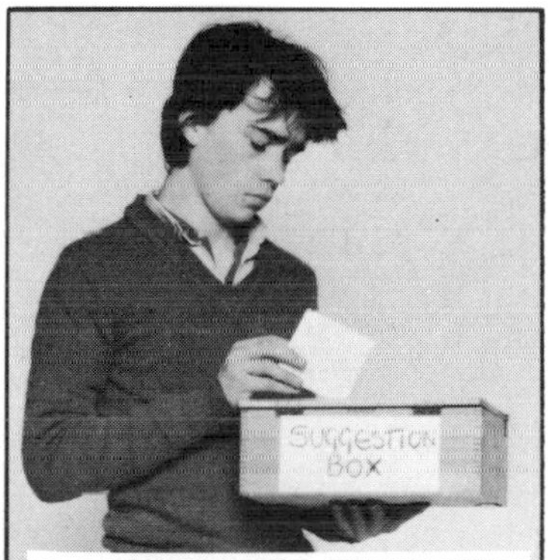

P. 19 FOOD FOR THOUGHT

P. 19 **Food For Thought** — chaos in the *Grange Hill* canteen!
P. 24 Pin-up of Benny
P. 25 **I Wish I'd Said That!** Excuses for every occasion ...
P. 26 Pin-up of Suzanne
P. 27 **Are Your Mates Worth Knowing?** Find out!
P. 28 Pin-up of Tucker, Susi, Cathy, Trisha and Alan
P. 30 **Not So Long Ago** ... What was school like for the stars?
P. 32 Pin-up of Pogo
P. 33 **School's Out!** Should you get a job at 16?
P. 34 **40 Questions** — test your knowledge of *Grange Hill*
P. 38 **No Sweat!** Solve all our puzzles!
P. 39 **The Great School Dinner Debate!** Is the food really bad?
P. 40 *Grange Hill* Calendar for 1982
P. 42 **The Long Search** ... Grid puzzles to fool you!
P. 43 **Take One!** The clues to a clapper-board
P. 44 **Making His Mark!** Learn all about Mark Baxter ...
P. 46 **Behind the Scenes —** with a make-up and wardrobe expert
P. 48 **Who's Top of the Form?** Maybe you are!
P. 49 Pin-up of Mr. Sutcliffe
P. 50 **Saturday Morning Fever** — detentions get right out of hand!
P. 55 Pin-up of Doyle
P. 57 **The Name Game!** How did Tucker get his nickname?
P. 58 Pin-up of Claire
P. 59 **Who's Bunking Off?** Duane Orpington — and he's in trouble!
P. 64 Pin-up of Paul McCarthy
P. 65 **A Testing Time!** How important are exams?
P. 66 **My Liverpool School.** Phil Redmond remembers his schooldays ...
P. 68 **Well, Now You Know!** Your rights as a pupil explained
P. 69 **A Lucky Break.** Another amazing picture story
P. 79 **Oh, Very Funny!** School jokes to tell your mates!

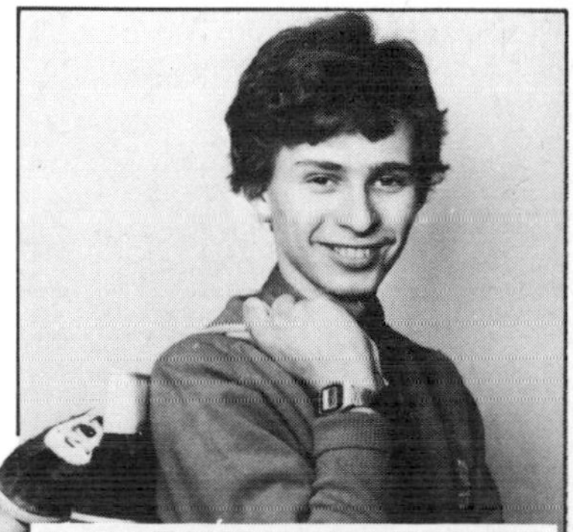

P. 44 AT HOME WITH MARK

the TELL-TALE STAMP

DURING LESSONS WOULD BE MORE APPROPRIATE! THAT'S WHEN THEY GO ASTRAY.
WOULDN'T CATCH MY LOT NICKING BOOKS. NONE OF THEM CAN READ.
Meanwhile . . .
LIKE SOME CHIPS, SIR?
MMM . . . TA!
HE SPAT ON THEM, SIR!
LEAVE IT OUT . . .
ANY BOOK BARGAINS GOING, I WONDER?
SECOND-HAND BOOK BARGAINS 30P — 90P.
HOI!
UH?
HOW'D YOU EXPECT ME TO SELL THAT AFTER YOU'VE COVERED IT IN CHIP FAT?
SECOND-HAND BOOK
OH, SORRY! DIDN'T THINK.
OLD MOANER! IT'S NOT AS IF THEY'RE BRAND NEW!
HEY, WHERE DID YOU GET THIS BOOK FROM?
DON'T ASK ME, MATE! I GET 'EM FROM ALL OVER THE PLACE.

GRANGE HILL SCHOOL LIBRARY
WELL THIS ONE CAME FROM ONE VERY PARTICULAR PLACE — MY SCHOOL LIBRARY!
SO?
THEY MUST'VE HAD A CLEAR OUT!
NOT OUR LIBRARY! NOW, ARE YOU GOING TO TELL ME WHERE YOU GOT THIS . . .?
. . . OR WILL I CALL IN THE POLICE?
Back in the staff room . . .
YOU CAN'T BAN CLASSES FROM USING THE LIBRARY! THERE'S NOWHERE ELSE TO GO!
WHAT YOU'RE SAYING IS WE'RE NOT SUPERVISING THE KIDS!
COOL IT, FOLKS! HAVE I GOT NEWS FOR YOU!
In the school corridor . . .
YOU'RE NOT ALLOWED TO BRING PETS TO SCHOOL!
IT'S NOT A PET! OUR CAT CAUGHT IT!

A BLOND BOY WEARING AN EAR-RING . . . WE'RE BOUND TO FIND SOMEONE WHO FITS THAT DESCRIPTION!
LOOK OUT! TEACHERS!
HELLO, WHAT ARE YOU TWO LOOKING SO GUILTY ABOUT?
NOTHING, SIR!
WELL, OUT YOU GO! NO-ONE'S ALLOWED IN SCHOOL 'TIL THE BELL GOES!
YES, SIR!
I'LL INFORM TEACHERS TAKING CLASSES IN THE LIBRARY!
YOU DO THAT.
PHEW! CLOSE CALL!
HEY, WHERE'S IT GONE? . . . MY MOUSE!
HASN'T ESCAPED THROUGH THAT HOLE, HAS IT?
Later that day . . .
SO NOW WE ALL KNOW WHAT THE THIEF LOOKS LIKE! BUT UNTIL HE'S CAUGHT, WE'RE NOT TAKING ANY CHANCES . . .
RRRINGGG!!
BEFORE ANY OF YOU LEAVES THIS ROOM, I WANT TO CHECK YOUR BAGS!
AW, MISS! . . .

. . . YOU'LL MAKE US LATE FOR OUR NEXT LESSON!
I'M SORRY, BUT I'VE GOT MY ORDERS!
DID YOU SEE BENNY HILL LAST NIGHT, AL?
YEAH! WHAT ABOUT THAT THING IN THE RED SKIRT, EH!
HEY, LOOK! A MOUSE!
FLIPPIN' 'ECK! SO IT IS!
GRAB IT, LADS! YOU GO ROUND THE BACK.
IT'S GOING UNDER THOSE CHAIRS!
JUST WHAT IS GOING ON OUT HERE? JENKINS . . . HUMPHRIES . . . GREEN . . . YOU'RE SUPPOSED TO BE AT MY LESSON!
WE'RE AFTER A MOUSE, SIR!
IT'S GONE BEHIND HERE! . . . WELL, IT DID A MINUTE AGO!
HMPH! I'VE HEARD SOME EXCUSES IN MY TIME, BUT . . . GET INSIDE!
A week went by, and then . . .
I GIVE UP! I REALLY DO! ANOTHER TWO BOOKS MISSING!
WHAT! BUT WE'VE BEEN CHECKING BAGS EVERY LESSON, MAUREEN!

WELL, SOMEONE HASN'T BEEN DOING THE JOB THOROUGHLY ENOUGH!
HONESTLY, IT MAKES ME DESPAIR TO THINK A WHOLE STAFF CAN'T CATCH THE LAD WHO'S BEHIND ALL THIS!
That afternoon . . .
SHIFT OVER A BIT, JENKINS!
SHIFT YOURSELF, DOYLE! I WAS HERE FIRST!
I'LL PUT THE WIND UP THAT DIMBO! WATCH THIS!
RRRINGG!!
JUST WAIT 'TIL THE BAG CHECK AT THE END OF THE LESSON!
OKAY, HAVE YOUR BAGS READY AS YOU LEAVE!
HUH! WHO'D PINCH BOOKS FROM THIS CRUMMY LIBRARY?
NOTHING TO DECLARE, MISS!
LET ME BE THE JUDGE OF THAT!

WHAT'S THIS THEN?
UH? HOW'D THAT GET IN THERE?
JUST WAIT THERE, JENKINS!
WAAAY, JENKINS! BEEN CAUGHT AT LAST, HAVE YA!
DOYLE! YOU RAT!
So, after school . . .
I SEE LORRAINE SMALLWOOD'S STILL GOING OUT WITH THAT CREEP FROM BROOKDALE
UGGH! GOT NO SENSE OF LOYALTY, HAS SHE!
DON'T TELL ME HE'S CARRYING HER BOOKS HOME!
DOESN'T LOOK THE TYPE, DOES HE!
HEY, HANG ON! BLOND HAIR . . . EAR-RING . . .
ARE YOU THINKING WHAT I'M THINKING? CAN'T BE . . .
HE FITS THE DESCRIPTION OF THE BOY WHO WAS SEEN SELLING THE LIBRARY BOOKS!
NO WONDER NO-ONE COULD FIND HIM AT GRANGE HILL

HEY, MISS! . . . MRS. HETHERINGTON!
YES, CATHY? WHAT IS IT?
FOUND THAT MOUSE OF YOURS YET, JOEY?
NAW! IT'S PROBABLY FOUND ITS WAY BACK HOME BY NOW.
But . . .
UGGGH! LOOK!
A MOUSE!
UGGH! KEEP STILL, OR IT MIGHT RUN ALL OVER THE PLACE!
DID I HEAR SOMEONE CRY 'MOUSE'?
OVER THERE, BY THE COOKER!
HEY, SO IT IS! JENKINS AND HIS MOB MUST HAVE BEEN RIGHT!

BETTER GET ON TO THOMSON ABOUT IT, OR YOU'LL HAVE THE HEALTH INSPECTOR DOWN ON YOU!
OH, GREAT! IS THAT ALL YOU HAVE TO SAY?
WELL, I CAN'T DO ANYTHING ABOUT IT! IT'LL ONLY RUN OFF IF I TRY TO CATCH IT!
THANKS A LOT – FOR NOTHING!
Outside, at that very moment . . .
DON'T THINK THEY'RE ON TO YOU YET, THEN?
NAW! NOT WITH THE LIKES OF DOYLE AND JENKINS IN MY CLASS! THEY'RE TOO BUSY WATCHING THEM!
LOOK, I'LL TAKE THIS LOT TO THE SHOP! THEY WON'T BE ON THE LOOK OUT FOR ME.
OKAY! IT'S ABOUT TIME YOU WORKED FOR YOUR CUT!
GOT SOME OLD BOOKS I WANNA SELL, MISTER.
CUTTING IT A BIT FINE, AREN'T YOU? I'M LOCKING UP.
I'LL TAKE THOSE, THANK YOU! THEY'RE NOT YOURS TO SELL!
HOI, WHAT'S GOING ON?

WHO SAYS THEY AREN'T MINE? THERE ARE NO MARKS ON THEM.
WRONG! HERE'S THE GRANGE HILL STAMP ON PAGE FORTY-SEVEN!
OBVIOUSLY, YOU DON'T READ ENOUGH LIBRARY BOOKS TO KNOW THAT'S OUR POLICY!
YOU CAN'T PROVE NOTHING!
HEY, JENKINS, YOU'VE BEEN SAVED!
YEAH, WE GOT YOU A REPRIEVE!
OKAY, TUCKER, OFF YOU GO HOME! THERE'S BEEN A MISTAKE!
BLIMEY! DID SHE DO IT THEN, MISS?
TAP TAP
RUN ALONG, THERE'S A GOOD LAD!
OH, I WILL! I'VE GOT SOME UNFINISHED BUSINESS . . .
DOYLE!! I'D LIKE A WORD WITH YOU!
HAAH! POOR DOYLEY! LOOKS LIKE HE'S BOOKED HIMSELF A GOOD HIDING!
THE END

A real mum, a Grange Hill mum and a chaperone can mean...

TRIPLE

Paula Ann Bland with Italia Conti's Mrs. Dean.

IF you ever get fed-up with being bossed around, spare a thought for the Grange Hill cast. Not only have they got two sets of parents and two sets of teachers (their real ones and the actors and actresses in the series), if they're under 16 they have a chaperone as well. Is it as bad as it sounds? We asked three of your favourites...

Paula's pretty happy!

"It's not bad at all," says Paula Ann Bland who plays Claire. "It makes the whole thing more exciting in a way," she laughs.

But doesn't she ever feel over-protected? Wouldn't she sometimes like to scream, "leave me alone!"

More laughter.

WORRY

"No, not at all," she explains. "My chaperone's fantastic. We get on really well. She never interferes, but I know she's always there to look after me. I suppose she takes over where Mum leaves off. She picks me up from school when I'm filming and takes me over to the BBC at White City to see I get there safely. She just generally helps me out. You know, if I've got any problems, I just have to ask her. And, oh yes, she always makes sure I get a proper dinner!

"Having two sets of parents does seem a bit strange. It's funny when you leave home after saying goodbye to your real mum and dad and then meet the TV ones. I was a bit nervous when I first met them. I remember hoping they'd be nice. But I needn't have worried. Even if they hadn't been, it wouldn't have mattered, because it's not like having real parents.

"One thing though, I wouldn't swop my real teachers for those at *Grange Hill*. The two schools are very different. And at Italia Conti, my stage school, the teachers are so much nicer. If you've got a worry, they listen to you. I'm not saying they're not strict — they are. But in a different way. I think if I went to a school like *Grange Hill*, I'd be quite scared."

'I WAS A BIT NERVOUS'

Susan's second mum!

Susan Tully, who plays Suzanne, doesn't mind having so many people telling her what to do, either.

"Why should I?" she asks. "It's great being looked after. My chaperone's really nice. She's not bossy at all. She's more like a friend. I think she looks after me really well. For example, I'm only allowed to work a certain number of hours a day. She keeps a careful check on that. And if I ever work two days in a row — she arranges for me to have a teacher on the set. It's like having a second mum.

"Apart from checking that I don't work too late, she worries about the small things, too. Like have I had a meal and am I tired. And she's always keeping an eye out to make

TROUBLE!

sure I'm being well treated.

"Mind you," Susan adds, "perhaps we wouldn't get on quite so well if we didn't like each other. I've never had a bossy chaperone. I'm sure I'd hate it if I did."

Susan herself goes to a comprehensive in Islington, North London, and believes the series is totally true to life.

"It's very typical of what goes on," she laughs. "Some of the bad things always get exaggerated, just like in real schools.

"But," she insists again, "having two sets of teachers doesn't get me down. It's the same with having two lots of parents. To be quite honest, you don't see much of your TV ones.

"My real school teachers never make a fuss about the series. They don't mind what I do as long as I keep up with my homework. Occasionally, I get a bit behind and panic. But then I just ring up my mates and they let

'IT'S MORE LIKE A HOBBY'

me copy work from their books. And then I study until I catch up again. The only subject I can't do that with is algebra. It's a bit too complicated.

"But I don't regard *Grange Hill* as work. It's more like a hobby. I love the atmosphere and the excitement. If I didn't enjoy every minute of it, I wouldn't do it. It's as simple as that. If I felt it was all getting on top of me — I'd say I'd had enough. But, thinking about it, my chaperone would probably tell me first."

Mr. Moran and Peter.

Susan Tully talking to her dad.

(The real one!)

Peter's a problem!

"I've got one of the nicest chaperones around!" says Peter Moran (probably better known to you as Pogo). "Well, she's great 95% of the time anyway. The thing is, she has to make sure I don't do anything really naughty and, well ... I can be a bit of a handful. It gets pretty boring waiting for a scene to be shot at times, so we all like to mess about a bit. I love playing football. Trouble is, I go all red and sweaty and that drives the make-up artist wild. She's always nagging me about it. I try not to listen ...

"But having two sets of teachers doesn't affect you at all. The *Grange Hill* teachers are all professional actors and it's all in a day's work for us. Most of the teachers at my stage school are all right, I suppose.

"Mum and Dad are all right, too. We live in a pub down the King's Road and Dad's always trying to get me to help. He goes on a bit about that. Oh yes — and Mum's always on at me to clean my bedroom. She gets really mad and throws my shoes downstairs and threatens to burn all my rubbish. It doesn't work, though. She usually ends up doing it herself.

"The problem is, I do try to be helpful — but it never quite works. She's got this brand new cooker — one of the hob sort — and as a surprise, I decided to clean it for her. Trouble is, I used detergent. She went potty. Well, how was I supposed to know you weren't meant to clean it that way?

BETTER

"I suppose I do get bossed about quite a bit really, but working on *Grange Hill* is great, I wouldn't change it a bit. Everyone's okay and I really like the directors. Also, it's 100% better than going to real school."

'MUM'S ALWAYS ON AT ME'

Peter Moran and his chaperone, Mrs. Merriman.

Please, Miss— I think I love you!

Falling for a teacher can be confusing, painful and very dangerous. And it could easily happen to you...

Remember Duane's crush on Miss Lexington?

FACT 1: Most people spend a lot of time thinking about the opposite sex.
FACT 2: For teenagers, a teacher is a popular figure to 'fall in love with'.
FACT 3: It may seem like the real thing — but it isn't. It's just a crush.
FACT 4: However bad you think you've got it — given time, you'll get over it!

Taking the above facts in turn, it's simple to see why it's so easy to become infatuated with a teacher.

Years ago, teachers could easily be distinguished from pupils by the way they dressed and looked. Today, it's not so easy. Casual clothes and hairstyles mean that they look just like the members of their school — and in a lot of cases, they're not much older!

CRUSH

You may fantasise about the girl at the bus-stop — or the boy in the butcher shop — but spending up to seven hours a day in school, you're just as likely to start fantasising about the people that you spend most time with. And if one of the people you fancy is a teacher — it's hardly surprising. He or she is in a position of respect — a person to be looked up to and admired. The problem is that often that admiration turns into infatuation.

If it happens, or has happened, to you, the first thing to do is not panic. Enjoy your feelings, live the fantasy out in your mind, but keep it to yourself. It won't seem like it at the time, but you are just experiencing a crush. And people always get over crushes. If you mouth off about it — it'll be embarrassing for you *and* your teacher. Even worse, it may lose him or her their job.

A teacher who is involved in any sort of scandal, true or untrue, runs the risk of a ruined career. No school will want to employ a teacher with a reputation — whether or not that reputation is deserved.

So how do crushes start? Quite often, without realising it, teachers can spark them off themselves. If, for example, a teacher starts to pay more attention to one particular pupil who's behind in their work, or a little slow to understand, that pupil may begin to believe he or she's been picked out for a very different reason. Every casual glance or reassuring touch is turned into a sign of affection. The pupil starts to worship the ground the teacher walks on — and there you've got it. The beginning of a crush.

GUARD

Other situations start when pupils are strongly attracted to teachers and want to believe that their feelings are returned. In a bid to get their teacher's attention, they make an extra effort with their appearance and try to be extra helpful. And when the teacher responds with a simple smile — that is taken as a good sign. He or she must fancy them, too!

The important thing to guard against is letting an imaginary — though seemingly real relationship — get out of hand. Don't keep a diary with details of how your favourite teacher touched your arm — or asked you to visit his or her house. Innocent incidents — or imaginary ones — could look very serious if the diary got into the wrong hands. Say, for example, your mother or father found it, you'd have a lot of explaining to do.

Also, if you start talking about your feelings, it'll be embarrassing for you and embarrassing for the teacher. The worse thing that could happen is that you'd find you'd told a series of lies about a relationship with a teacher and you're in so deep you can't back down. Real-life cases of crushes that have got out of hand often result in the teacher being suspended and eventually dismissed.

CLEVER

But what happens if you've got a crush on a teacher of your own sex? Don't panic. There's nothing wrong with you. These feelings are perfectly normal. You may admire Debbie Harry because she's pretty and talented — or Gary Numan because he's good-looking and clever — but that doesn't mean you necessarily fancy them. In the same way, you may admire a teacher because they seem to be everything you're not. Capable, clever and good company. It doesn't matter that they're the same sex. You'd look up to anyone with all those qualifications.

Teacher crushes can last a couple of weeks or a couple of years. They normally stop quite naturally, often because the pupil involved finds a boyfriend or girlfriend of their own age — or because they just grow out of it. However bad you feel, remember you're not the first person to go through the agony of a crush — and you won't be the last. You *will* get over it.

MARK BAXTER (DUANE ORPINGTON)

BIRTHDAY: 21st May, 1965 **STAR SIGN:** Gemini
HAIR: Light brown **EYES:** Blue **HEIGHT:** 5′7″
SISTERS: None **BROTHERS:** 1 younger one
PETS: 78 goldfish, a dog, a cat, 3 budgies and a hamster
HOBBIES/INTERESTS: Football **MUSIC:** Pop music
AMBITION: To carry on acting after finishing school
OTHER APPEARANCES: Mark played Oliver in a stage musical, has worked on some commercials and had a part in *Search & Rescue* (HTV) and *Headmaster* (BBC)

RENÉ ALPERSTEIN (PAMELA CARTWRIGHT)

BIRTHDAY: 30th June, 1964 **STAR SIGN:** Cancer
HAIR: Light brown **EYES:** Blue/grey **HEIGHT:** 5′6″
SISTERS: 1 older **BROTHERS:** None **PETS:** None
HOBBIES/INTERESTS: Enjoys horse-riding and is taking a course at a stage school which involves tap, ballet and jazz
MUSIC: Likes pop music very much and loves shows and films
AMBITION: To carry on acting professionally
OTHER APPEARANCES: René has appeared in many television commercials as well as *Grange Hill*

A Grange Hill Story

FOOD FOR THOUGHT

When the local chippy burnt down, it was a disaster for Tucker and Co. How could they face the boring canteen? It was a dump in comparison!

AS soon as the bell rang for the end of morning lessons, the race was on to be first in the queue at the chippy. Normally, Tucker Jenkins and his mates won it comfortably, but today they'd been given a talking to by Miss Peterson for messing about in class, and that gave them a five minute handicap.

"Blimey, Joe'll be out of sossies," Tom Watson muttered as he did an Allan Wells out through the school gates, past the telephone kiosk by the bookies, past the greengrocers, in and out of the bus queue that was taking up half the pavement — and up to the doorway of Joe's chippy itself. There, he stopped and stared.

His three companions weren't far behind. They'd less reason to hurry now that they knew there'd be a queue. Tucker and Alan could afford fish with their chips, whereas Tom had to settle for a couple of sausages. And they went fast because they were only 12p. Benny, on the other hand, didn't hurry because he couldn't afford anything with his chips — and there was always plenty of them.

Suddenly, Tucker stopped and looked back. It had just occurred to him that everyone else was going in the opposite direction — minus their usual steaming, vinegar-soaked wrappers with their chippy smells. Something was up.

"Here," said Tom, as they caught up with him. "Take a look at that."

They could hardly take it in at first. Instead of the familiar neon-lit grime green and rust, with tiles to match, Joe's chippy had been transformed overnight into a blackened, windowless shell.

"Blimey! They've had a fire!" Benny gasped.

"Brilliant!" Alan sneered. "We didn't think it was the new decor!"

"No wonder everyone's heading back towards school," said Tucker, making tracks in that direction himself. "They've gone to the canteen."

Unfortunately, the chippy fire had caught the school canteen on the hop as well. It wasn't prepared for the sudden rush of new customers who descended on the place like locusts, buying up any spare grub going. Attendances at school dinners had been dropping, so stocks of food had been trimmed to avoid waste. Consequently, by the time Tucker and Co. got there, all the hot food had gone. It was cheese sandwiches or nothing.

"Some flaming fast-food service this is," Alan complained to Mrs. Simmons, who was serving behind the counter. "It can't even rustle up a few decent sandwiches at short notice."

"Well, if you'd been here earlier," she apologised, "you could have had a hamburger, a hot dog or a cup of tomato soup."

The rest of the meal was spent moaning at Susi McMahon's table. Alan had gone over to join her and Pamela Cartwright, and the others followed him.

"Why did you come here if you hate it so much?" Susi asked Tucker who was finding fault with just about everything.

"Don't worry, you won't be

All the hot food had gone by the time Tucker arrived. Only cheese sandwiches were left.

FOOD FOR THOUGHT

"If you'd been here earlier, you could have had a hamburger, a hot dog or a cup of tomato soup."

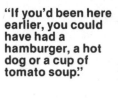

seeing me in here again!" he replied.

But Tucker found himself eating his words as well as his school meal the very next day. When he'd gone home the night before, he'd left it too late for his mum to buy in stuff for making sandwiches. Not that she was keen on having to make them, anyway.

The same went for Tucker's three cronies. So the very next lunchtime found them all sharing a table with Susi, Pamela, Justin Bennett and Andrew Stanton. Although they'd all managed to get hot grub this time, the chippy regulars still reckoned the school canteen wasn't much cop.

"Then why don't you suggest ways of improving it?" Pamela urged.

"No point, is there. We'll be out of here, soon as the chippy's back in action."

"And how long will that be?" asked Andrew.

"Couple of months. Maybe less," said Alan, who knew a little about the building trade.

"Maybe more," said Justin. "You're going to be using this place for a good few weeks, at any rate. So why not try to get some fresh ideas going?"

"Yes, Alan, why not?" pleaded Susi. "Look, us four are in a sort of committee, organised by Mr. Gillespie. We're meant to find out all sorts of ways of improving school meals."

"Trouble is," Justin intervened, "we've run out of new ideas."

"Well, don't look to us for any," said Benny, draining a can of Coke. "We don't know anything about organising meals and all that."

"All we know about is going down the chippy!" grinned Tom.

"Well, there you are then," Susi blurted, surprising them all. "That's a start."

"What do you mean?" asked Alan.

"You can tell us why you go there."

"For the grub, of course! What do you think, dimbo?" Benny shook his head at the stupidity of the question.

"What about the food in here? You reckon it's not as good."

Tucker took over as spokesman for his little group.

"It's better than it used to be, I'll give you that."

"But not enough to tempt you back regularly?" Pamela asked.

"Nope."

"Well, anyway, we're working on that. Next month, we hope to have chips on the menu, just like McDonald's in the West End."

"Supposing the food here was as good as the chippy's," Justin interrupted. "Would you come here then?"

"Doubt it," Tom shrugged, nicking a chunk of hamburger off Alan's plate. "This place has got no atmosphere, has it. I mean, the chippy's got music and that."

BIG IDEAS

"Yeah," Benny chipped in. "A juke box. *And* Space Invaders!"

The four committee members looked at each other across the table. They seemed excited by the idea. Why couldn't they have these things here in the school canteen? It'd bring people in by the dozen. Yes, Tucker and his mates should definitely suggest it to Mr. Gillespie. After all, it was their idea. They should take the credit.

"I'm not going up to Gozzie and suggesting Space Invaders," Tucker scowled. "You do it, Benbo." But all four were reluctant to take on the job.

Susi solved the problem by pointing out that they could write down their ideas and pop them in the suggestion box in the school entrance hall. Mr. Gillespie emptied it each day.

That idea appealed to them and off they went, adding other suggestions to the list as they went along. Tucker thought topless waitresses would do the trick, until Alan pointed to Mrs. Newland and that changed his mind. Well, a go-go dancer then, he thought. The one his dad had been disgusted by in his lunchtime pub.

As the foursome left the canteen, the occupants of the table next to theirs turned and watched them go.

"A juke box and Space Invaders, eh!" said Michael Doyle. "Sounds not a bad idea. Might go and see Gozzie myself after lunch."

"Jenkins will murder you if you pinch his suggestions, Doyley," Macker warned. "Think of something else."

"Why should I," Doyle called back to him, "when they've laid it on a plate for me!"

★★★★★★★★★★★

With a major food supplier in the area temporarily crocked, it wasn't long before the Pogo Patterson Catering Service was back in business. There were bound to be a few hungry ex-chippy-goers mooching about the playground, Pogo reckoned, so with reckless disdain for his mum's kitchen supplies, he plunged back into baking rock cakes and scones. He even entered the sweets market, too, since he'd heard complaints about the prices at the tuckshop. Slabs of candy were easy enough to make, and squares of cooking chocolate looked like the real McCoy wrapped in tin foil.

"Ten pence a packet," he told Suzanne Ross, offering her a quarter pound of candy splinters in an old sweet box.

"Get lost, Patterson," she scowled at him. "I wouldn't buy your home-made rubbish!"

"'Tisn't rubbish! It's good stuff! Here, taste a bit," he urged, opening the pack and thrusting it towards her. A free sample might boost business.

"Mmm," she slurped, pleasantly surprised. "Not bad."

Pogo gave her a few more seconds. "Worth ten pence, isn't it!" he said.

"Mmmm. Maybe, but I'm broke!" she smiled. "Byeee!" And she trotted off yelling across the playground. "Hey, everybody, Pogo Patterson's giving away free candy!"

Pogo gaped in horror as all eyes turned on him. Then he hared off round the science block.

Mr. Thomson watched him race past, pursued by a gang of howling third years. "Blooming hooligans," he muttered to himself. "Knock you over soon as look at you." He wasn't in the best of moods. On top of his normal worries, he had mice to contend with. Laid down traps and poison all around school, he had, following a complaint by one of the cookery teachers that she'd mice in her classroom. And how many mice had he caught to date? None. Next time, he'd tell her to get her eyes tested.

Hello, he sniffed, watching Tucker Jenkins and Alan Humphries emerging from the canteen. Betcha they're up to no good. You could tell by the way they were plotting, heads together.

Mr. Thomson's fears were unjustified. Tucker and Alan were on their way to find out about their suggestions for the canteen. It was almost a week since Tucker had posted them in the suggestion box, but they'd heard nothing since.

"*Your* suggestions?" Mr. Gillespie scoffed when they confronted him. "Michael Doyle's, you mean. He came to me with them days before you handed in your list."

"Doyle!" Tucker snarled as he left Gozzie's room, branded a rip-off merchant. "That little ***," Tucker cursed. "He must've got wind of what we were up to! Just wait till I get him!"

"Told you to get that list in right away, didn't I?" Alan shrugged, annoyed with Tucker for taking two days to get down to doing it. "Now we've made Doyle the blue-eyed boy! Touch him and you can guess whose side Gozzie'll take."

Alan was right. They could do nothing about it, apart from telling Doyle what a rat he was. But he knew that already.

It was no consolation to them, either, to learn that their ideas had gone down well with several members of staff and even the school's governors. Mind you, the reason for the latter's approval was pretty obvious.

Doyle had gone home and bragged about his brilliant ideas in front of his father who, of course, just happened to be one of the board of governors. Like father, like son, the old man had few ideas of his own and latched on to any good ones that he found going spare. So it was that the suggestions made by Tucker and his mates came to be passed on à la Doyle to the powers that be. A mixture of persuasion, bribery and outright bullying obtained a small majority in favour of the innovations.

"I won't have it," was the Head's reaction when the vote was carried. "You can't realise the implications of introducing such things into the school!"

"Taste a bit," Pogo urged, opening the packet. A free sample might boost business. Suzanne Ross was pleasantly surprised.

FOOD FOR THOUGHT

Arguments against the proposal were sound but outgunned. It was time, the governors felt, for innovation and experiment. Something had to be done to make the system pay.

★★★★★★★★★★

Three weeks later, with the canteen staff prepared for a bigger than usual influx of customers, the machines arrived — and the place was packed out.

"I was here first!" yelled Stewpot Stewart, clinging to the front of the Space Invaders console as Matthew Cartwright tried to barge in front. The queue behind them was twenty deep.

"No, you weren't, Stewart. Get out of it!"

"What was that you asked for?" Mrs. Simmons asked, leaning over the counter to catch the latest order. It was hard hearing what was being said in a canteen where Madness was the order of the day. "Oh, can't someone turn that thing down," she called at last in desperation, glaring daggers at the juke box.

Mr. Mitchell dashed to lower the volume and was rewarded with loud protests from the paying customers.

"Aw, sir!" I paid ten pence to hear that!"

"I want my money back!"

"Don't listen to him, sir! He only used a foreign coin, anyway!"

It was a sign of things to come.

Susi and Pamela were making their way to the canteen when they passed Tucker and Alan, sulking outside.

"Aren't you coming in?" Susi asked. "After all, they were your ideas."

"Not any more, they're not," Alan moaned. "We didn't get the credit for suggesting them."

Pamela sighed and looked at the sky.

"Look, just because Doyle got there before you, there's no reason to sulk. A good idea is a good idea, no matter who came up with it."

"She's right," said Susi. "Now are you coming for something to eat or are you going hungry?"

The two protestors shrugged, waited until the girls had gone in and then followed.

"Hope the whole thing's a disaster," muttered Tucker as he joined the food queue. He glowered at Doyle who was enjoying the instant success of his scheme.

"I'm next," he was saying, as he pushed Claire Scott away from the juke box. "My idea, wasn't it!"

"Got any change, sir?" asked Precious Matthews.

Mr. Hopwood groaned. He'd been asked that question dozens of times already. "I'm sorry, Precious," he said, keeping his calm. "You'll have to try someone else."

Queues were beginning to run into other queues so that it was hard to tell who wanted a hamburger and who wanted to put a record on the juke box. He dashed over to sort that lot out.

Tucker and Alan joined Benny and Tom who were having a good laugh about it all.

"Hey, who's that at the door?" Benny asked. "The bloke in the raincoat with the tape recorder."

They all looked. A thin, gawky bloke with thick, bottle-glass specs was talking to one of the first year kids. The kid seemed to be talking into the microphone.

SCOOP STORY

"I'm from the local paper," the chap told him. "Heard about these new machines in your canteen. What do you think?"

"They're great," came the reply, and the reporter moved on to someone else.

"What about you, son? You don't look too happy," he said to Duane Orpington, inviting him to reply into the mike.

"Spent all me money, haven't I," Duane shrugged.

"Not your meal money, surely," the reporter gasped, amazed by his good fortune at hitting upon such good story material.

As Duane accounted for one pound and twenty pence spent on the juke box and on Space Invaders, Jim McIntosh, ace reporter, was already composing the headline in his mind: SCHOOLKIDS GO HUNGRY WHILE SCHOOL PROFITS!

"Excuse me," said Mr. Hopwood, butting in. He'd been watching Mr. McIntosh for some time and had only just realised what his game was. "Have you got permission to be in here?"

The reporter tried to bluff his way out but found himself being ushered to the door and ejected.

"I'm sorry, but rules are rules. You must obtain permission from the Head first," Hopwood apologised.

"Pah! Okay, I'll go," McIntosh growled. "I've got more than I expected anyway."

The balloon went up next morning. With the appearance of the article in the local paper, the phone rang non-stop in the Head's office. Irate parents were up in arms about their children's dinner money going to waste. Governors disowned the whole project. National daily newspapers wanted to know more. Education Authority officials demanded explanations.

The Head dealt with all the enquiries calmly and efficiently, putting people at ease and promising that the matter would be looked into straight away. And it was. Unfortunately, the new machines could not be got rid of as the first month's rental hadn't been paid and the last thing anyone wanted was for them to make a loss. So, notices went up in the canteen, limiting each pupil to spending 50p on the machines — and only after producing a meal ticket to show that they were having a meal.

"Typical," Trisha Yates complained. "What about us who only come in here to play the juke box? Does that mean we can't?"

Trisha and Cathy Hargreaves had started dashing back from their usual lunches at home so that they could stop in the canteen and listen to the records. Now, it seemed, they could listen only to other people's choices.

It came as something of a relief to the staff of *Grange Hill* when the Space Invaders machine broke down and had to be taken away for two days. Kids complained and demanded their lunch money back, saying they'd only dined in the canteen so they could play Space Invaders.

Quarrels erupted over the choice of records on the juke box. Pogo Patterson didn't help matters by playing a Police record three times on the trot and then complaining loudly to Mr. Hopwood when Tom Watson pressed the reject button.

But the death blow came a fort-

Susi suggested that they wrote down their ideas and popped them in the school suggestion box. Mr. Gillespie emptied it each day.

night after the newspaper article appeared. Canteen staff arrived to open up one morning, only to find that someone had opened up for them. A window had been smashed open and the store room door pushed in, leaving the cash-filled machines at the raiders' mercy. Not satisfied with robbing the cash boxes on both machines, the intruders had taken great delight in dismantling the costly machinery itself.

Mr. Gillespie and members of his School Meals Committee were among the first people to knock on the Head's door following the decision to abandon the entertainments scheme.

POP MUSIC

"We haven't come to beg for their reintroduction," Susi McMahon explained, before the Head bawled them out. "We just want your permission to try an alternative idea."

It was hardly the time to bother the Head with new suggestions, since the old ones were still fresh, but nevertheless they were given a fair hearing.

"What we're saying is, music in the canteen attracted a lot of pupils to the place." Justin Bennett tried to put the argument as convincingly as he could. The Head agreed with that statement. "And so we'd like to keep having music in the canteen."

The Head asked how they proposed to do that.

"Well, we thought we could try a system adopted by another school which we read about in the newspapers," added Pamela. "It means borrowing a school record player and having someone playing records during lunchtime.

"A sort of disc jockey, playing requests. Kids could bring their records and we'd play them."

"Not too loud, of course," Andrew Stanton pointed out. "And the teacher on duty would be there to keep an eye on things."

An hour later, it had been agreed to try the new system. But, the Head stated quite emphatically, if there was the slightest sign of trouble, that would be that. It was only the healthy increase in the numbers attending school meals which gave them all a second chance.

★★★★★★★★★★

"Blimey, what's that Tom-Tom's carrying in his dustpan?" Andrew Matthews asked as he saw the caretaker heading for the bins behind the canteen. A lid was lifted and the contents of the dustpan emptied inside.

"Let's go and look," said Richard Steel, his first year classmate.

They raced to the bin as the caretaker vanished into the building.

"Hey, it's a mouse!"

They gazed at the shrivelled, grey creature which lay, open-eyed but seeing nothing. Then they looked at each other.

"Wonder if it could be your one?" Andrew pondered.

"Naw, mine was bigger, much healthier than that."

"Can't look healthy when you're dead, can you," Andrew mocked. "Anyway, it's been eating school meals. What do you expect?"

They looked round to see a group of third years carrying a record player, microphone and stand, as well as a bundle of LP's into the canteen.

DINNER DISCO

"Must be the new disco thing," Richard observed.

Susi McMahon was horrified. "You mean, you aren't coming?" she exploded. "Not even to see me as deejay?"

Alan wanted to, of course, but he was outvoted, three to one.

"Chippy's open again," he explained. "That's where we usually go, isn't it!"

His three mates nodded. Susi's face was bright red.

"That's great, that is," she raved. "Here's us going to all this bother to make the canteen better and off you lot go the minute that smelly chippy reopens!"

Pamela Cartwright was anxious to know more.

"We thought you liked the food now," she said.

"It's okay," they agreed.

"And the music, too?"

"Yeah, don't mind that, either," said Tucker.

"Then what's wrong with the canteen now?" Susi fumed.

"Got teachers, hasn't it!" Benny shrugged. "Can't do nothing about them."

With that, the four lads turned and dashed out of the playground, leaving the girls speechless.

"Hey, Doyley," Tucker shouted, spotting his arch-enemy sloping off for his daily hamburger. "Your old man seen you yet? Thanked you for those ideas, has he?" He laughed out loud. Doyle scowled back. It was the last time he'd listen to any of Jenkins's stupid suggestions. Might have known they'd be disastrous ...

THE END

TERRY SUE PATT (BENNY GREEN)

BIRTHDAY: 29th September, 1964 **STAR SIGN:** Libra
HAIR: Black **EYES:** Hazel **HEIGHT:** 5′2″
SISTERS: 2 **BROTHERS:** 3 **PETS:** None at the moment
HOBBIES/INTERESTS: Playing football and most sports
MUSIC: Likes pop music very much
AMBITION: He's not sure whether he'd like to carry on acting but he does enjoy attending stage school
OTHER APPEARANCES: *Blind Man's Bluff* (film), *General Hospital* (ATV), *Jackanory* (BBC) and many other parts

I WISH I'D SAID THAT!

Ever been in a tight spot and wished you could talk your way out of it? Well, wish no more, 'cos here we present the complete **Grange Hill Good Excuse Guide** ***that'll make sure you'll never be tongue-tied again!***

1. Your homework's not done again, and that cane-happy teacher is coming round the class! Help! You're not going to get away with it this time — unless you think fast! Don't panic! Just —

A Say, "Well, I was on my way to school this morning when this *huge* dog leapt on me out of nowhere! 'Course, I had to fend it off with something, and all I had was my exercise book. I knew you'd rather I saved my life than my homework, wouldn't you?"

B Stare blankly at the pages of your book and mumble, "I was so intent on getting all my thoughts down on paper, I just didn't notice my pen needed filling ..."

C Say, "I left my exercise book lying around and Mum used it to line the bottom of the budgie's cage. You can have it if you *really* want it, but you'll have to wrestle the budgie first!"

2. You didn't think anyone would notice if you arrived at school ten minutes late, but the Head is standing waiting for you by the gate! Stop worrying! Just relax, smile, and simper —

A "Don't tell me I'm late? I've been making my own digital watch and I still haven't got the prototype quite right. Oh, well, back to the drawing board ..."

B "I wasn't feeling very well this morning, so I thought I'd crawl along and tell you I'd be away today. The fresh air's made me feel much better, though, so I hope it's okay if I don't go home ..."

C "I left my house in plenty of time, but what with lollipop ladies and muggers and everything, I got slowed down ..."

3. It's P.E. again! Yes, it's all happening on the sports field — which is why you're hiding out in the boiler house! Only trouble is, you've just been discovered! As you stand there, shivering in your gym shoes, now's the time to exercise that brain of yours! The answer's easy! Just say —

A "I was just warming up my leg muscles, doing a bit of running!" (In the opposite direction, of course!)

B "I wanted to encourage the other kids — they just get discouraged when I'm around, I'm so good ..."

C "You mean, this isn't the games field? Oh, no, don't say my blackout attacks are starting again?"

4. You're all passing notes in class. You've just written a really good one on the subject of the teacher's bad breath — when suddenly you realise it's nearer than you thought — right down your neck, in fact! If you can keep a straight face, you can get out of it! Just explain —

A "I was just correcting these terrible spelling mistakes! By the way, how *do* you spell 'amazing' ...?"

B "I think this is for you, it's got your name on it ..."

C Nothing! Actions speak louder than words — just eat the evidence!

5. You think you look great in your fluorescent ankle socks and green dungarees — but unfortunately they're not quite school uniform! And funnily enough, the teachers seem a bit funny about that sort of thing. So, if you want to avoid a dressing down, what do you say for yourself? How about —

A "Well, I've just come back from rehearsals for the school play actually. I'm a fluorescent tree ..."

B "It was the Head's idea — I'm testing out a new uniform. I'll say you don't like it, if you like!"

C "Our house burnt down last night and all my clothes with it! These belong to my cousin ..."

6. You're bouncing a first year in the corridor when suddenly you feel a big, icy hand on your collar. As you fly through the air, you see 'Masher' Smith, the school bully — and the first year's brother! Help! You quickly explain —

A "I was just giving a few lessons in self-defence — it's amazing how these little kids can get set upon ..."

B "You know, I could have sworn I saw a deadly Bug Beetle on his collar — I was just saving a life!"

C "Your bruv said something rotten about you—I just couldn't let the toad get away with it ..."

SUSAN TULLY (SUZANNE ROSS)

BIRTHDAY: 20th October, 1968 **STAR SIGN:** Libra
HAIR: Light brown **EYES:** Blue **HEIGHT:** 5'1"
SISTERS: 1 baby one **BROTHERS:** 1 younger **PETS:** None
HOBBIES/INTERESTS: Reading, sewing, swimming, roller-skating
MUSIC: Her favourite group is Police
AMBITION: She doesn't know what she'd like to do when she leaves school, but at the moment she takes drama lessons
OTHER APPEARANCES: *Saturday Banana* (Southern), *Our Show* (LWT) and *Why Can't I Go Home* (ATV)

YOU'VE GOT TO HAVE FRIENDS . . .

but are your mates worth knowing?

Here's a test to prove who your real friends are! Try this quiz — it should take you all of five minutes! — and find out whether you've got great mates — or a bunch of bad buddies!

1 The school bully has singled you out for rough treatment. Everyone's scared of the brute — 'specially you! Would your mates —

A Try to stick up for you?
B Tell someone else about the problem — a teacher, or the person in charge?
C Run away?

2 You're bunking off school with a couple of mates — and both of them are caught. Would they —

A Give you away immediately — why should they suffer alone?
B Rely on you to own up?
C Say nothing at all, and suffer the punishment on their own?

3 You went to see the mid-week match, or spent the night bopping at the disco, and you've clean forgotten some *very* important home-work! Would your mates —

A Lend you theirs to copy straight out?
B Help you with the answers?
C Refuse to help you! Serves you right for going out and enjoying yourself!?

4 You've worn your new leather jacket to school to show everyone — and you're called to see the Head. You know the strict rules about uniform — and you could be expelled! Would your mates —

A Enjoy seeing your face as you disappear into the Head's office! It's no skin off their nose?
B Lend you a blazer for five minutes?
C Help you think up an excuse for the Head?

5 One of your mates has written a note saying nasty things about the teacher, and is passing it round the class. You're just reading the message when the teacher catches you — and accuses *you* of writing it! Would the culprit —

A Own up straight away — why let you take the blame when it's not your fault?
B Only own up when it looks like you're going to be punished?
C Keep quiet about it — if they can get away with it, why not?

6 You're taken ill and have to have a fortnight off school — trouble is, you're missing a lot of important work. Would your mates —

A Volunteer to come round to your place every night to keep you up to date on what's going on, so you don't fall behind?
B Wait until you come back to school, then help you to catch up?
C Do nothing to help you — they hardly do any work themselves, so how could they?

7 You've missed the bus and you're going to be late for school. This particular morning, the Head's doing a spot check on timekeeping — everyone who's late will be kept in for an hour! Would your mates —

A Cover up for you until you get to school?
B Deliberately make themselves late so they can stay in with you after school?
C Make sure everyone knows you're late — serves you right if you *do* get kept in!?

8 You're tempted to do a spot of shoplifting just for a thrill. Would your mates —

A Encourage you to do it, 'just for a laugh'?
B Try to stop you going ahead but let you take your own risks?
C Put a stop to you being foolish by warning someone in charge, even though they know it might make you angry?

See score on page 38 . . .

Grange Hill

From left to right ...

Michelle Herbert (Trisha Yates) was born on 11th May, 1965. She has brown hair, blue eyes and a brother called Kevin. Her pet dog is called Jupiter and she enjoys cooking, sewing and knitting. Madness, Police, The Lambrettas and The Beat are her favourite pop groups. She'd like to act full-time.

★★★★★★★★★★★

Lyndy Brill (Cathy Hargreaves) has brown hair and blue eyes. Born on 30th July, 1963, she hopes to be a successful singer as well as an actress. Lyndy has a brother called Leigh and a sister named Julie, but no pets. Earth Wind & Fire, Donna Summer, Michael Jackson and Barbra Streisand make her kind of music.

★★★★★★★★★★★

Todd Carty (Tucker Jenkins) is a West Ham supporter and enjoys football, tennis and swimming. He was born on 31st August, 1963 and has two sisters — Billy Jo and Bobby Sue. His hair is dark brown and his eyes are hazel. Todd passed his driving test first time and is mad about driving. He also loves animals an awful lot.

★★★★★★★★★★★

Linda Slater (Susi McMahon) likes ELO's music and can cook, paint, swim and draw. Her ambition is to be an actress and appear in a musical comedy. Linda's pet poodle is called Nicky and her ginger cat answers to Goldy. Born on 8th November, 1963, Linda has fair hair and green eyes.

★★★★★★★★★★★

George Armstrong (Alan Humphries) likes rock 'n' roll — especially Buddy Holly and Bill Haley. He is blond with hazel eyes and has a brother who's younger than him. George enjoys cricket, rugby and other sports, too. When he's not going to drama lessons, you might find him feeding his pet goldfish quietly at home!

The stars remember their schooldays!

Not So Long Ago...

You may not be able to imagine this lot in school uniform, but they remember being pupils pretty well!

PHIL WAS A FIGHTER!

Phil Lynott and Brian Downey of Thin Lizzy went to school together in Dublin. "One day, one of the school bullies picked on me," Phil remembers, "I think he was just jealous 'cos we were already in our own group then. He gave me a good going over and afterwards I got ready to give him a return fight after school!

"Trouble was, Brian saw this guy warning his mates and getting them to come along. We knew we'd be outnumbered, but there was nothing we could do.

"Outside the gates there were five of them waiting for just Brian and I! I'm happy to tell you though, we gave them all a beating and they never bothered us after that!"

A SURPRISE FOR THEREZE!

"No one told me I'd won a prize for the best essay at school!" Thereze from Dollar told us. "So it came as a shock when the headmistress read my name out! She wanted me to go up and collect my prize, only I was sitting right at the back of our big school hall!

"If I'd known, I would have sat at the front. It took me about three minutes to get to the stage, while everyone just waited in silence. The only things that you could hear were grunts and groans as I stood on people by accident while I struggled to the front!"

GAME FOR ANYTHING JIMMY!

Jimmy McNicholl was a whizz at sports when he was at school.

"It was definitely my best subject and I figured my games teacher wouldn't say anything if I took the day off. Me being the apple of his eye and all that.

"The next day I brought a note from my mum saying I'd been ill.

"My teacher soon found me out, though. The football game I'd been to see was shown on telly, and there I was — for all the world to see — cheering and having a good time!

"There was some sport the next day, I can tell you!"

DENNIS THE MENACE!

"I really was a terror at school!" Dennis Waterman smiled. "I started acting when I was 11, but I still had to have a certain amount of lessons.

"I didn't really care about learning my tables or spelling, so I used to bring frogs and spiders as presents for my teacher and put nails on her chair!

"I must have been a right little horror!"

CLIFF LOST OUT!

"I wanted to be a singer when I was 14," Cliff Richard told us. "I used to practise curling my lip like Elvis Presley in my mirror at home!

"But I'll never forget losing my prefect's badge. My headmaster found out that I'd gone to see a Bill Haley concert!

"I was in disgrace with everyone for about a month just because I went to a concert! They never gave me my badge back, either!"

DAVE DIDN'T DO MUCH WORK!

"I really used to like school!" Dave Sparrow of The Photos told us, "and I was pretty good in most subjects. Then my parents gave me a guitar and I got interested in that! I used to spend as much time as I could practising and taking guitar lessons, so my homework really suffered.

"One day, my form teacher passed me in the corridor. When he asked me why I was standing around when I should have been in class, I explained I'd been sent out 'cos I'd been misbehaving, and it was true!

"It was a music lesson, which was one of my worst subjects!

"I saw my teacher the other day — he came to one of our concerts!"

PETER MORAN (POGO PATTERSON)

BIRTHDAY: 16th July, 1967 **STAR SIGN:** Cancer
HAIR: Red **EYES:** Blue **HEIGHT:** 5'4"
SISTERS: None **BROTHERS:** None **PETS:** Unknown
HOBBIES/INTERESTS: He plays the saxophone and takes regular lessons to improve his playing **MUSIC:** Lots of different sounds
AMBITION: Hopes to continue acting when he's left school
OTHER APPEARANCES: Peter was only five when he started his career, so he's done quite a lot! He's been in *Star Wars* (film), *David Copperfield* (BBC) and *The Likely Lads* (BBC)

SCHOOL'S OUT!

If you're thinking of leaving school, here's all you need to know!

FIRST off, if you're not yet 16 — forget it! The law says that you've got to stick with studying until you are actually 16. Even then there are certain conditions. Namely, if your sixteenth birthday is between September 1 and January 31, you can leave at the Easter after your birthday. If your birthday is at any other time, you have to wait until the end of May.

Now that's sorted out, it's worth thinking about the advantages — and the disadvantages of leaving.

Obviously, a big problem is the very high risk of being unemployed when you leave school. However much you think you dislike school now, if you're out of work with nothing to do all day, no money to spend and even worse — no prospect of a job — your school days will suddenly seem like a much happier time.

That said, even if you do stay on until you're 18 or go on to university (and gain lots more qualifications), you could still end up without a job and find yourself at the end of the unemployment queue, with the people who left at 16 in front.

LUCKY

You may, however, be lucky and find a job. And the kind of job you want should help you to decide whether or not to stay on.

The positive advantage of leaving school early is that you can gain the one thing that most employers are looking for — experience. A lot of firms juggle between employing staff with experience or inexperienced staff with lots of qualifications straight from school. Often experience wins.

But another factor of high unemployment is that employers can be choosier. And if they can find someone with qualifications AND experience, that's the person they'll be more than likely to choose.

Basically, if you've decided on a career, your next step is to find out what qualifications are demanded for the job, and at what age you can start. If a firm stresses that qualifications are preferable — but not compulsory — don't chance your luck. Stay on and study.

It is true that some companies actually prefer to train youngsters on the job, though. And, if that is the case, you'd do far better getting in there as soon as possible.

PROMOTED

Take the time to speak to your careers officer and find out what qualifications are needed for the job you have in mind. This should have the most influence over whether or not you decide to stay on.

You'll hear a lot of people say that exams aren't everything. They are right. If you're not the right person for the job, you won't get it. It's as simple as that. But, as mentioned earlier, now employers can afford to be more choosy, you'll stand more of a chance with qualifications.

The advantages of leaving school early are (if you get a job), a lot more freedom, money of your own, no homework, no bossy teachers or school rules. The disadvantages are that later on you may regret not having more qualifications when you see other people being promoted above you. And you will still have to put up with bossy bosses and stupid company rules.

The advantages of staying on at school are that you don't have to join the employment race for another two years or more; and when you do, you could well be in with a better chance. The disadvantages are that you'll still be dependent on your parents for money and you won't have the same freedom that your school-leaving mates have.

One good rule to guide you is that if you really have no idea what you want to do, stay on at school. The extra years will probably help you to decide and stop you from turning into a drifter. The kind of person who changes his or her job because of 'boredom,' 'lack of interest' or just because they 'feel like a change,' isn't popular with prospective employers. So, if in doubt, stay on!

On the other hand, if you know what you want to do, but have to wait until you're 18 or so to start, you may be better off at college. Certainly, if you're thinking of going into office work as a clerical worker or secretary, any time spent at college studying shorthand, typing, business studies like book-keeping, accounts, etc., will give you a clear advantage over someone who's spent just one hour a week bashing an ancient school typewriter.

REGRET

If you're not academically minded — and you know that the extra two years would just bore you silly, leave as soon as you can. Lots of jobs don't require qualifications of any sort (and not just the dead-end ones) so check with your local Job Centre.

If, after leaving, you regret your decision and wish you could train for something, the government scheme T.O.P.S. can help you. To qualify, you have to be at least 19, unemployed or willing to give up your job, and have been out of full-time education for at least three years. The Training Opportunities Scheme will train you in a vocation that you must, of course, intend to take up afterwards. What they can't do is guarantee you a job, but the training — in a field of your choice — should stand you in good stead.

40 QUEST

Series 1

1. Can you name the original six characters in the show? Were they ...
a) Tucker, Trisha, Benny, Justin, Judy Preston and Anne Wilson?
b) Tommy, Cathy, Susi, Tucker, Benny and Booga?
c) Justin, Tucker, Doyle, Brian Smith, Judy Preston and Pogo?

2. What happened to Judy Preston?
a) She was off sick with a mysterious illness?
b) She left *Grange Hill* to go to *Brookdale*?
c) She was suspended for stealing?

3. Who was the first sports master at *Grange Hill*?
a) Mr. Thomson?
b) Mr. Sutcliffe?
c) Mr. Foster?

4. Do you remember the original six characters' first form teacher? Was it ...
a) Miss Peterson?
b) Mr. Mitchell?
c) Mr. Redmond?

5. When did Michael Doyle arrive at *Grange Hill*?
a) At the very beginning, he was in the first show?
b) Episode 7 of the first series, he'd been very ill?
c) Episode 2 of the first series, he had been playing truant?

6. Who broke a leg in the first series?
a) Justin?
b) Tucker?
c) Alan?

7. How did he do it?
a) He got run over by a car?
b) Booga Benson broke it in a fight?
c) He fell off a factory roof?

8. Who stole the Flintlock pistol?
a) Benny?
b) Trisha?
c) Doyle?

9. And who made the culprit return it?
a) Tucker?
b) Alan?
c) Mr. Sutcliffe?

10. What happened to Tucker and Benny after they broke into the factory?
a) They were caned by the Head?
b) The police arrested them?
c) They got locked in and couldn't get out?

CONS

Special Grange Hill Quiz

Have you watched Grange Hill since the very beginning? Do you know the series so well you could answer almost any question about it? Okay, well here's your big chance. See how you do with this bumper quiz!

Series 2

1. What happened at the beginning of the second series?
a) The school library was burnt down?
b) Mr. Llewellyn re-organised the school?
c) The gym floor was ruined?

2. Who joined form G1?
a) Cathy Hargreaves?
b) Booga Benson?
c) Susi McMahon?

3. Trisha started to teach someone to read. Who was it?
a) Michael Doyle?
b) Tommy Watson?
c) Simon Shaw?

4. Why didn't he know how to read? What was wrong with him?
a) He'd missed a lot of lessons when he was younger?
b) He'd been completely blind until he was six?
c) He was dyslexic?

5. Who broke into the school and accidentally set it on fire?
a) Booga, Doyle and Justin?
b) Benny, Alan and Simon?
c) Trisha, Cathy and Susi?

6. What do the initials S.A.G. stand for?
a) Students' Action Group?
b) School Archery Group?
c) Students' Art Group?

7. Why was the S.A.G. formed?
a) Fifth formers wanted to abolish school uniform?
b) The Head wanted to introduce a new sport?
c) Third formers demanded extra art lessons?

8. Why did *Grange Hill* pupils get a special day off?
a) The school was shut down for redecorating?
b) The teachers went on strike?
c) A gas leak had to be investigated?

9. What happened to Cathy Hargreaves on that day?
a) She had an accident and lost her memory?
b) She lost her keys and got locked out of her house?
c) She was caught shoplifting?

10. Later in the term, what happened to Benny's blazer?
a) It was stolen by the Brookies?
b) He brushed against wet paint and ruined it?
c) Tucker tore it in half?

40 QUESTIONS (Continued)

Series 3

1. Who arrived on bikes for their first day at *Grange Hill*?
a) Pogo and Mark?
b) Suzanne and Claire?
c) Duane and Tracy?

2. Which form did they go into and who was their form teacher?
a) Mr. Sutcliffe?
b) Mr. Baxter?
c) Miss Mooney?

3. Why did Madelin Tanner get expelled?
a) For stealing bikes?
b) For bunking off?
c) For hitting a teacher?

4. Why did Penny Lewis get in trouble about the school magazine?
a) She spent too much money on producing it?
b) It was full of terrible spelling mistakes?
c) She wrote a nasty article about Doyle?

5. What was Benny's football problem?
a) He couldn't decide whether to play on the left side of the pitch or the right?
b) He had to choose whether to play for the school or the district when matches clashed on the same day?
c) His boots had been stolen and he didn't have any to wear on the pitch?

6. Who was G3's new form teacher?
a) Mr. Thomson?
b) Miss Peterson?
c) Mr. Sutcliffe?

7. Who was R3's form teacher?
a) Miss Peterson?
b) Mr. Baxter?
c) Mr. Hopwood?

8. How did Pogo and Duane make extra money for themselves in a clever way?
a) Doing other people's homework at fifty pence for an hour's slog?
b) Selling cakes?
c) Washing cars?

9. Why was Susi embarrassed at school one day?
a) She burped in the middle of a lesson?
b) Her skirt fell down around her ankles in the middle of a busy corridor?
c) Alan and Andrew saw her taking off her bra?

10. What happened to Antoni Karamanopolis?
a) His parents took him away from *Grange Hill* because they didn't approve of the school and thought he was bullied?
b) He was killed when he fell off a wall?
c) Tucker saved his life when he got cramp at the swimming baths?

Series 4

1. What happened to *Grange Hill* at the beginning of the fourth series?
a) It was vandalised?
b) The gym burnt down?
c) A burst water pipe flooded the ground floor?

2. Who beat up Tucker Jenkins?
a) Michael Doyle?
b) Alan Humphries?
c) Booga Benson?

3. Who was found drunk at school — and why?
a) Andrew Stanton — his mum and dad separated?
b) Tucker Jenkins — he was feeling fed-up?
c) Michael Doyle — he'd been celebrating his birthday down the pub with his mates?

4. Who won the competition to design a new school magazine?
a) Cathy Hargreaves?
b) Tommy Watson?
c) Tucker Jenkins?

5. Who became Susi McMahon's boyfriend?
a) Alan Humphries?
b) Michael Doyle?
c) Tommy Watson?

6. What did Tucker nag Alan to do?
a) Lose some weight?
b) Give up smoking?
c) Pack Susi up?

7. Who was the teacher who hit Stewpot?
a) Mr. Baxter?
b) Mr. Sutcliffe?
c) Mr. Hicks?

8. Who were the star turns at the school dance?
a) Bright Star and his Twinkles?
b) Sooty and the Sootettes?
c) Throbbing Gristle?

9. What was the contest being decided at the end of the series?
a) Whether boys are better than girls?
b) Whether *Grange Hill* is better than *Brookdale*?
c) Whether teachers are smarter than pupils?

10. What was the result of this competition?
a) It's still not been decided yet?
b) A draw because both sides cheated?
c) All the votes were disqualified?

THE ANSWERS

SERIES 1
1-a, 2-b, 3-c, 4-b, 5-b, 6-a, 7-c, 8-c, 9-a, 10-a.

SERIES 2
1-b, 2-a, 3-c, 4-c, 5-b, 6-a, 7-a, 8-b, 9-c, 10-a.

SERIES 3
1-c, 2-c, 3-a, 4-c, 5-b, 6-b, 7-c, 8-b, 9-c, 10-b.

SERIES 4
1-a, 2-c, 3-a, 4-c, 5-a, 6-b, 7-c, 8-b, 9-a, 10-b.

AWARD YOURSELF FIVE POINTS FOR EACH CORRECT ANSWER!

0-65: What's your excuse, then? That you've only just begun watching *Grange Hill*? Sounds like a pretty weak one to us! Hope you'll become a real *Grange Hill* fan now!

70-135: Mmmmm...not bad, but you could have done much better! Okay, so your memory's not so great, but this is one exam that should be fun!

140-200: Well done, *Grange Hill* fan! Especially if you got maximum marks! As you no doubt agree, *Grange Hill* is such a terrific programme, it's easy to remember what's been going on. You know everything there is to know about Tucker and the rest of the *Grange Hill* pupils.

NO SWEAT!

Have a go at solving these extra special school puzzles!

Sum dominoes

Doyle and Tucker were in dead trouble after being caught playing dominoes during a maths lesson. Their puzzling punishment was to move the dominoes so that each side added up to 17 points — while keeping the same square shape. See if you can do it! They were seeing dots in front of their eyes before they'd finished!

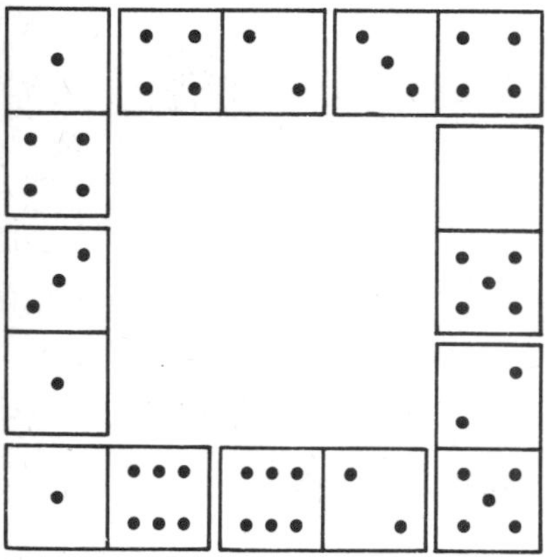

Ages to do

Suzanne, Pogo and Claire are in a bit of a muddle — so try to solve this problem of their ages! We'll pretend that Suzanne is older than Pogo by as many years as Pogo is older than Claire. Claire is half as old as Pogo was when Pogo was half as old as Suzanne is now. In a year's time, the combined ages of Claire and Pogo will equal that of Suzanne!

Report it!

Any one of a number of *Grange Hill* pupils could have got this report. Try to rearrange the letters of each word to make sense. Luckily, the teacher has a sense of humour!

A quick clue — the first word is 'Has'.

MATHS	Ash lfeanl espeal a nrbeum fo sitem!
ENGLISH	lpyt eh ntac arde!
WOODWORK	Leyarl nhtsa a ugel!
MUSIC	Nyvoreee ehre snitkh ehs nteo feda!
ART	Douslh vgei hsit jutbesc eth uhbsr-fof!
HISTORY	Sih nmdi wasayl esmes no a fretefidn iprdoe!

Time kids, please!

There were cheers when the school clock went on the blink — until Mrs. McClusky produced an hour glass. Here it is showing six different times — can you discover the correct order? It's not as difficult as it looks!

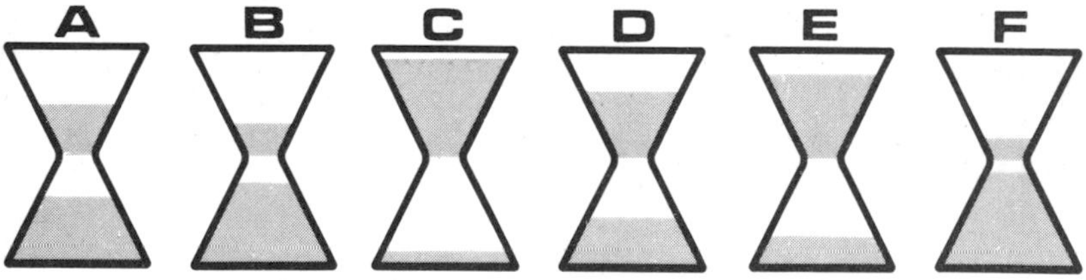

Be on your metal

Can you fill in the missing letters on the metalwork shop blackboard to complete the names of eight metals? Go on — have a go and see!

1 _ _ P _ E _
2 _ _ N _
3 I _ _ _
4 S _ E _ _ L
5 B _ _ _ S
6 _ O L _
7 _ R _ N _ E
8 _ I _ _ E _

His & Hers

Look down the class register of boys' names and then make a list of the equivalent girls' names.

Christopher	✓	✓	–
Frank	✓	–	✓
Gerald	–	✓	–
Jack	✓	✓	✓
Joseph	✓	✓	✓
Leslie	✓	–	✓
Nicholas	✓	✓	✓
Patrick	–	✓	✓
Paul	✓	✓	–
Robert	–	✓	✓
Stephen	✓	✓	✓
Terry	✓	–	✓

Answers on page 79 . . .

The great school dinner debate!

Traditional school dinners are being replaced by cafeteria snacks in many areas. And if the comments of these* Grange Hill *fans are anything to go by, that idea will be greeted with cheers from dining rooms up and down the country!

Are they really so awful?

Back to nature

I dread the summer coming because I know salads will start appearing again on the school menu. Last year I counted three caterpillars, a couple of slugs and an earwig nestling snugly in my lettuce. It made lunch-time seem like a biology lesson.

Mandy, Birmingham.

Chef's special

I never thought our school meals were too bad till I made an amazing discovery. I took a tray of plates into the kitchen one day, and found all the cooks busily noshing. But not for them the watery stew they'd served us — every single one of them was tucking into a plateful of their own home-made sarnies!

Darren, Swindon.

Weighty problem

At our school you can't eat the lunches without putting on weight. You either have a choice of stodgy steak and kidney pud or greasy hamburger and chips. So if you're on a diet, it's impossible to get a nourishing meal that doesn't pile on the calories. The only solution is to go hungry!

Anna, Harlow.

Keep it, Mum!

I don't know why everybody complains so much about the standard of school meals. I think they're wonderful — but then so would you if you had to eat the stuff my mum dishes up every night!

Mark, Wigan.

Ever thought of suggesting that your mum gets a job as a school cook?

Thanks for nothing

As ours is a church school, we always have to say Grace before meals. But have you ever heard over three hundred voices chanting, "For what we are about to leave, may the pigs be truly grateful"? It's true — the food's so bad that even the pigs would have to force it down!

Sarah, London.

Health food?

If anyone needs evidence that school food isn't exactly doing you a power of good, just look round the dining room. People with spots, bad teeth, or weight problems outnumber the healthy-looking ones. Whoever it was who said, "You are what you eat" must have been reared on a diet of school food!

Julie, Hastings.

My big mistake!

My friends think I'm crazy. I'm pointed at in the corridor, whispered about in class and laughed at on the school fields. Have I got three heads? No. All I did was admit one day that I quite liked school dinners!

Brett, Leicester.

Quick — call the school nurse. This boy's sickening for something!

Nutjob
I NEVER WANT TO SEE YOU EATING IN CLASS AGAIN, NUTJOB!
MMM... WON'T TAKE A MINUTE
OKAY, NOW THERE'S NO PROBLEM!

The GRANGE HILL

January

Su		3	10	17	24/31
M		4	11	18	25
Tu		5	12	19	26
W		6	13	20	27
Th		7	14	21	28
F	1	8	15	22	29
Sa	2	9	16	23	30

February

Su		7	14	21	28
M	1	8	15	22	
Tu	2	9	16	23	
W	3	10	17	24	
Th	4	11	18	25	
F	5	12	19	26	
Sa	6	13	20	27	

May

Su		2	9	16	23/30
M		3	10	17	24/31
Tu		4	11	18	25
W		5	12	19	26
Th		6	13	20	27
F		7	14	21	28
Sa	1	8	15	22	29

June

Su		6	13	20	27
M		7	14	21	28
Tu	1	8	15	22	29
W	2	9	16	23	30
Th	3	10	17	24	
F	4	11	18	25	
Sa	5	12	19	26	

September

Su		5	12	19	26
M		6	13	20	27
Tu		7	14	21	28
W	1	8	15	22	29
Th	2	9	16	23	30
F	3	10	17	24	
Sa	4	11	18	25	

October

Su		3	10	17	24/31
M		4	11	18	25
Tu		5	12	19	26
W		6	13	20	27
Th		7	14	21	28
F	1	8	15	22	29
Sa	2	9	16	23	30

CALENDAR 1982

March

Su		7	14	21	28
M	1	8	15	22	29
Tu	2	9	16	23	30
W	3	10	17	24	31
Th	4	11	18	25	
F	5	12	19	26	
Sa	6	13	20	27	

April

Su		4	11	18	25
M		5	12	19	26
Tu		6	13	20	27
W		7	14	21	28
Th	1	8	15	22	29
F	2	9	16	23	30
Sa	3	10	17	24	

July

Su		4	11	18	25
M		5	12	19	26
Tu		6	13	20	27
W		7	14	21	28
Th	1	8	15	22	29
F	2	9	16	23	30
Sa	3	10	17	24	31

August

Su	1	8	15	22	29
M	2	9	16	23	30
Tu	3	10	17	24	31
W	4	11	18	25	
Th	5	12	19	26	
F	6	13	20	27	
Sa	7	14	21	28	

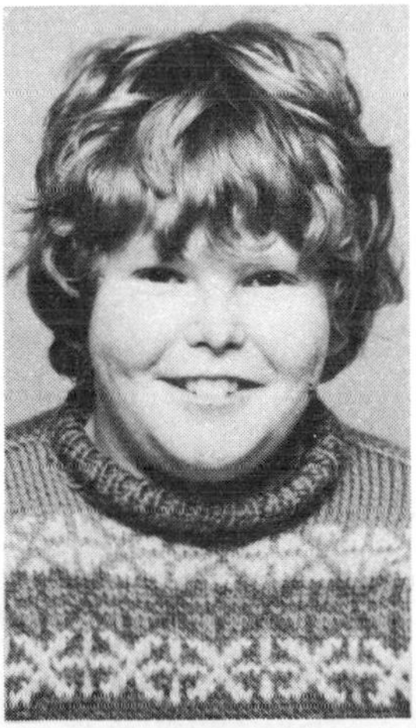

November

Su		7	14	21	28
M	1	8	15	22	29
Tu	2	9	16	23	30
W	3	10	17	24	
Th	4	11	18	25	
F	5	12	19	26	
Sa	6	13	20	27	

December

Su		5	12	19	26
M		6	13	20	27
Tu		7	14	21	28
W	1	8	15	22	29
Th	2	9	16	23	30
F	3	10	17	24	31
Sa	4	11	18	25	

THE LONG SEARCH...

Got a few hours to spare? Then get to grips with these grids! Find all the words!

IT'S A LESSON!

P	A	L	P	H	Y	S	I	C	A	L	E	D	U	C	A	T	I	O	N
H	I	S	T	O	R	Y	G	S	K	H	M	I	A	G	I	H	E	T	O
T	I	E	U	I	T	Y	A	O	C	U	A	K	D	E	X	S	J	A	I
A	S	R	A	N	E	T	K	N	A	I	S	S	U	R	A	O	U	W	T
V	M	U	Z	B	X	N	E	E	D	L	E	W	O	R	K	V	I	M	C
H	A	T	R	A	C	R	H	R	B	D	O	N	U	Q	A	E	F	C	U
E	F	A	O	W	F	M	O	C	Y	A	G	L	C	A	P	S	A	L	R
S	Q	R	A	D	E	J	E	U	H	F	E	P	O	E	P	Y	A	B	T
H	U	E	P	E	M	A	J	T	P	E	N	A	R	O	L	T	H	E	S
T	S	T	E	C	H	N	I	C	A	L	D	R	A	W	I	N	G	A	N
A	C	I	I	R	A	S	E	L	R	L	B	I	X	N	E	Z	E	G	I
M	I	L	N	A	M	R	E	G	G	I	W	B	A	A	D	A	G	T	S
R	T	H	N	A	T	U	K	R	O	W	D	O	O	W	M	F	R	J	U
E	A	S	W	I	P	W	U	L	E	I	C	O	R	Z	A	A	L	E	O
T	M	I	A	Y	U	S	O	S	G	D	A	Y	N	K	T	O	R	H	I
U	E	L	K	V	E	G	E	O	M	E	T	R	Y	F	H	K	C	D	G
P	H	G	P	H	Y	S	I	C	S	J	I	P	E	M	S	A	D	I	I
M	T	N	V	I	T	A	R	O	Y	R	T	S	I	M	E	H	C	B	L
O	A	E	G	A	U	G	N	A	L	H	S	I	L	G	N	E	Z	A	E
C	M	X	A	E	C	N	E	I	C	S	C	I	T	S	E	M	O	D	R

Twenty-eight subjects on the school curriculum are hidden here, written either forwards, backwards, vertically, horizontally or diagonally. Try to spot them all and write them down before checking against the answer.

Applied Maths
Art
Biology
Chemistry
Computer Maths
Domestic Science
Drama
English Language
English Literature
French
Geography
Geometry
German
~~History~~
Latin
Mathematics
Metalwork
Music
Needlework
~~Physical Education~~
Physics
Pottery
Religious Instruction
Russian
Science
Spanish
Technical Drawing
Woodwork

THEM AND US!

Try to find eighteen pupils and staff of *Grange Hill* hidden in this grid. Some letters are used more than once, others not at all. Cross off each one as you find it — but don't get too cross if you don't spot them all!

Mr. Baxter
~~Justin Bennett~~
Pamela Cartwright
Michael Doyle
~~Benny Green~~
~~Michael Green~~
Cathy Hargreaves
~~Mr. Hopwood~~
~~Alan Humphries~~
Tucker Jenkins
Penny Lewis
Mrs. McClusky
~~Susi McMahon~~
Mr. Sutcliffe
Andrew Stanton
Tommy Watson
~~Trisha Yates~~

N	E	E	R	G	L	E	A	H	C	I	M	S	A	R	P	U	A	M	C
O	L	P	G	A	L	A	N	H	U	M	P	H	R	I	E	S	J	A	U
H	Y	E	A	D	B	E	N	N	Y	G	R	E	E	N	N	O	T	Q	A
A	O	H	B	M	Y	I	A	P	O	E	C	A	G	E	N	H	L	E	P
M	D	A	I	D	E	L	I	E	T	R	I	S	H	A	Y	A	T	E	S
C	L	F	E	C	K	L	W	X	D	O	B	I	V	H	L	K	E	F	N
M	E	Y	Z	T	A	N	A	X	E	A	A	H	A	U	E	N	I	F	I
I	A	K	J	O	M	B	C	C	F	N	U	R	X	O	W	A	F	I	K
S	H	S	A	M	R	V	E	P	A	D	G	T	A	D	I	U	E	L	N
U	C	U	F	M	O	I	B	E	U	R	W	O	C	E	S	R	Z	C	E
S	I	L	I	Y	F	A	G	N	E	E	T	L	E	K	B	T	E	T	J
G	M	C	A	W	Z	P	K	A	M	W	M	W	Y	A	I	B	G	U	R
I	E	C	K	A	E	T	V	O	E	S	V	J	R	J	H	L	A	S	E
A	J	M	D	T	S	E	I	Y	L	T	E	N	T	I	S	M	H	R	K
H	U	S	E	S	S	H	V	A	W	A	K	O	A	R	G	K	E	M	C
E	M	R	H	O	P	W	O	O	D	N	A	L	P	I	Y	H	F	U	U
L	C	M	R	N	U	Y	I	T	E	T	Q	W	E	T	A	N	T	I	T
A	O	A	N	E	W	A	R	O	X	O	U	A	S	O	G	Z	B	E	O
J	B	E	Q	U	O	T	T	E	N	N	E	B	N	I	T	S	U	J	D
S	U	Z	A	N	N	E	R	O	S	S	R	E	V	A	Z	E	C	I	A

Answers on page 79 ...

Can you understand a clapper-board?

TAKE ONE!

You've probably seen a clapper-board at some time or another, but have you any idea what one is for? Well, for a start, the 'clap' that a clapper-board makes allows the technicians to match the sound and film exactly. This is a great help to them when the film is being 'edited', cut and trimmed to make the final version.

But there's also quite a bit of information actually written on the board itself. In the example shown, this is what it tells you:-

The scene being shot is for *Grange Hill,* you can see that quite clearly.

Proj. 03340-9025 is the code number given to it by the BBC and that's the number that goes onto the computer.

Dir. S. Hellings shows that the director of the scene is Sarah Hellings.

Ep. 6, of course, means it's for episode six.

815 1 tells you what scene and 'take' it is. So you're about to shoot scene 815, first take.

Cam. M. Southon — the cameraman's name is M. Southon!

You are also bound to realise that actors and actresses have a script to learn for each episode of a series. But what you probably don't know is that there are several versions of the same script — four or more, in fact.

First of all, the writer does the first version, as he would like to see it recorded. Then, in discussion with the producer and director, this is changed slightly — or quite a bit — for various reasons. The script may work out too long, parts of it may be boring — or there could be complicated production problems.

The next script is the one used for rehearsal. **(See below.)** This might stay as it is, or be changed in parts if problems show up while it is being rehearsed.

From the rehearsal script, a camera script is drafted. **(See below.)** This has the final dialogue and instructions for the cameramen and sound operators. The episode is recorded, and that's it, isn't it? Nope, not quite. At the BBC, a transmission copy is done of most programmes. This means that every word spoken is taken down and typed up into a 'transmission script'. This is similar to the camera script, but details may differ.

If any viewer has a query or complaint about a programme, the point in question can immediately be checked on the transmission script!

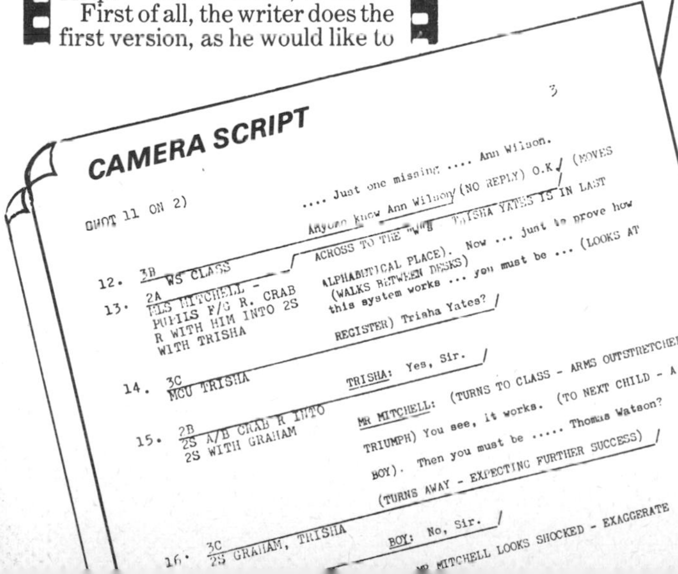

CAMERA SCRIPT

3

SHOT 11 ON 2)

.... Just one missing .... Ann Wilson.

Anyone know Ann Wilson (NO REPLY) O.K. (MOVES ACROSS TO THE "W"s – TRISHA YATES IS IN LAST ALPHABETICAL PLACE). Now ... just to prove how

12. 3B WS CLASS

13. 2A MLS MITCHELL – PUPILS F/G R. CRAB R WITH HIM INTO 2S WITH TRISHA

(WALKS BETWEEN DESKS) this system works ... you must be ... (LOOKS AT REGISTER) Trisha Yates?

14. 3C MCU TRISHA

TRISHA: Yes, Sir.

15. 2B 2S A/B CRAB R INTO 2S WITH GRAHAM

MR MITCHELL: (TURNS TO CLASS – ARMS OUTSTRETCHED – TRIUMPH) You see, it works. (TO NEXT CHILD – A BOY). Then you must be ..... Thomas Watson? (TURNS AWAY – EXPECTING FURTHER SUCCESS)

16. 3C 2S GRAHAM, TRISHA

BOY: No, Sir.

MR MITCHELL LOOKS SHOCKED – EXAGGERATE

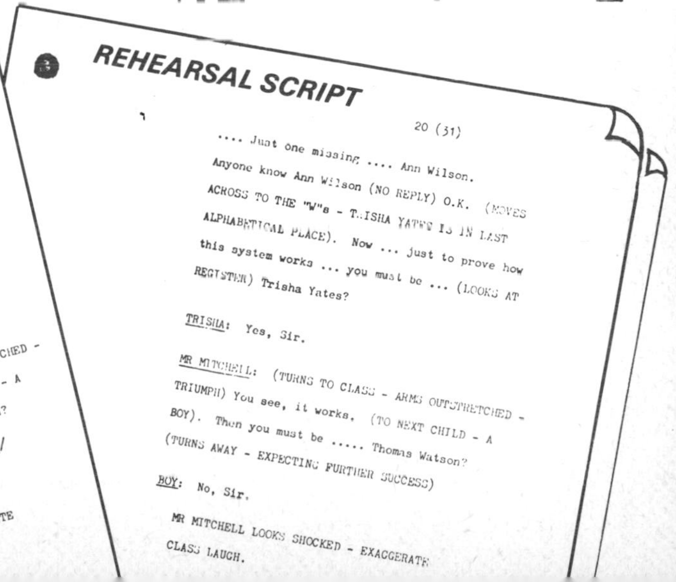

REHEARSAL SCRIPT

20 (31)

.... Just one missing .... Ann Wilson.
Anyone know Ann Wilson (NO REPLY) O.K. (MOVES ACROSS TO THE "W"s – TRISHA YATES IS IN LAST ALPHABETICAL PLACE). Now ... just to prove how this system works ... you must be ... (LOOKS AT REGISTER) Trisha Yates?

TRISHA: Yes, Sir.

MR MITCHELL: (TURNS TO CLASS – ARMS OUTSTRETCHED – TRIUMPH) You see, it works. (TO NEXT CHILD – A BOY). Then you must be ..... Thomas Watson? (TURNS AWAY – EXPECTING FURTHER SUCCESS)

BOY: No, Sir.

MR MITCHELL LOOKS SHOCKED – EXAGGERATE CLASS LAUGH.

Another Grange Hill star…

MAKING

"I get on great with my mum, Jill. She gives me lots of encouragement. All the family do — especially my grandad. He never missed one performance of *Oliver*."

IT was a lucky break that got Mark into acting. Or, to be more precise, a broken leg at the age of seven…

He was advised to take dancing lessons because the exercise would do him good, so he joined a stage school and hasn't looked back since.

Acting is in Mark's blood. His grandad appeared in the Whitehall Theatre, London, just after the Second World War, and is today one of Mark's greatest fans.

He didn't miss a single performance of *Oliver* when Mark played the title role in 1977/78.

FAMILIAR FACE

And if you think Mark's face looks very familiar — you're right. He's appeared in numerous TV commercials advertising everything from sweets and bread to washing powder and drinking chocolate.

Now he plays the role of Duane in *Grange Hill*, of course — a part he really enjoys.

"It's so nice to work with people of my own age," Mark says. "Older people can be a bit condescending sometimes, but we all have a great time together.

"It's fun and it doesn't take up as much time as people imagine. Most of the filming is done during the school holidays."

Even so, he's a very busy lad. But all the work doesn't stop him finding time for his many hobbies. Mark's football mad. And a great Liverpool supporter.

"Even if I can't get to their matches, I wear my Liverpool top," he says. "I did manage to get to a recent game in Brighton, but it's difficult because I've got a Saturday job in Woolworth's." That doesn't stop him playing football in his spare time though, or playing darts at a mate's house in Hanwell.

Nor does it stop him from going out to a disco most Saturday nights. "I used to like skating, too!" he laughs. "On rollers and on ice — but I had a bit of an accident and ruined my jeans, so I'm off it at the moment. A bit too painful!"

Next to acting, it's obvious Mark's love is for sport. He's good to boot, as the many certificates and cups in

Mark keeps all his certificates and cups in his room. He's earned them for swimming, diving, running and football.

On Monday night you'll find Mark out with the lads. The Lads' Brigade, that is! It's an organisation attached to the church.

HIS MARK!

Besides being a pretty good actor, Mark Baxter's a talented sportsman, too. Want to know more about this athletic fella? Then here's your chance ...

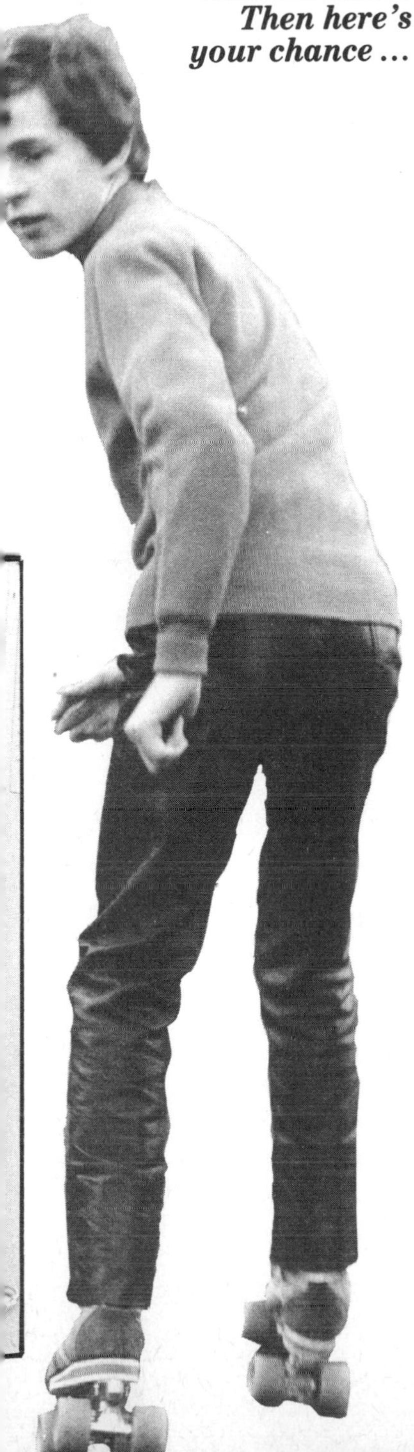

his bedroom show. Swimming, diving, running, football — you name it — Mark's got an award for it! He gets lots of good exercise in each week at the Lads' Brigade which he always attends regularly. There he does a bit of everything — from playing the gazoo and the drums in a band, to practising football and gymnastics. There are girls in the group, too — and they all parade in church once a month. Mark's been a member for just over a year and a bit altogether.

NO GIRLFRIEND

Mark says he gets quite a bit of fan mail "particularly from girls, not love letters — just asking for my autograph usually" and, in case you're wondering, no Mark hasn't got a girlfriend at the moment. He did have one, but that finished a while ago. "I'm a free fella," he explained.

He lives with his family including younger brother, Joey and Alsatian, Storm, in Acton, West London, and plans to leave school very soon.

And he's in no doubt about what he wants to do.

"Carry on acting, of course," he says. "I love it. I don't know what parts I'll get, I have to leave that to my agent. But I don't mind what I do. I'm prepared to take anything that comes along. That's what's so nice about my work. I never know what I'll be doing next. It's exciting and I know I wouldn't want to do anything else."

Keep up the good work, Mark!

Younger brother, Joey, aged 10, challenges Mark to a game of spin football in his room. "But," says Mark, "I usually win. I'll have to watch out, though — he's getting better all the time."

Storm is the family's two-and-a-half year old Alsatian. She's very lively and needs lots of exercise. "I don't take her for walks though," admits Mark. "I leave that to Mum."

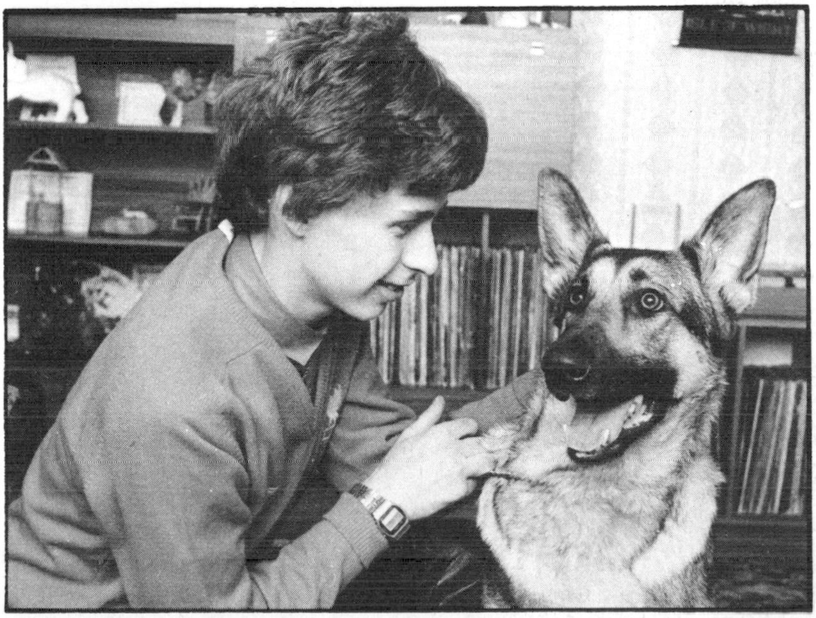

Take a peep... BEHIND THE

Uniform is optional at *Grange Hill* which means that within the set guidelines, pupils can wear what they like. So actors and actresses are given suitable outfits to wear in the series and the person behind that important choice is Irene Whilton.

IDEAS

"After I've talked to the director to discover how he sees the characters," she told us, "I chat to the individual children who are playing the parts.

"We get together and discuss the personalities and from that discussion I decide on the costume. They've all got set ideas on how they think they should look and, so far, I've been lucky. We've all agreed.

Spots are Maureen Winslade's biggest problem. That — and continuity.

"Very little actual make-up is used on *Grange Hill*," Maureen told us. "A lot of my time is taken up in de-spotting. Blemishes always appear worse on screen than they do in real life because the colour is more exaggerated. I have to soften the colour and gently blend it into the rest of the skin."

The spots themselves aren't the real problem. In fact, they probably make the programme more realistic. After all, how many teenagers do have clear skin all the time?

The real problems start when the same scene is continued a few days later when a spot has newly emerged or disappeared completely.

"That's why I always camouflage them," says Maureen. "Much easier than actually painting one on. You run the risk of getting the wrong position — and then we'd be knee-deep in letters from observant viewers!

"Hair lengths have to be consistent, too. We take lots of Polaroid shots — particularly at the beginning of the series — to make sure we don't make any howlers. Natural growth can obviously be allowed for, but we do try to discourage the actors from changing their hair-styles mid-series unless it's part of the script. Some of them do get a little bored, so watch out for fresh styles in the next series. There are bound to be some alterations to suit the story as well as the individuals.

MAUREEN WINSLADE
Senior Make-Up Artist

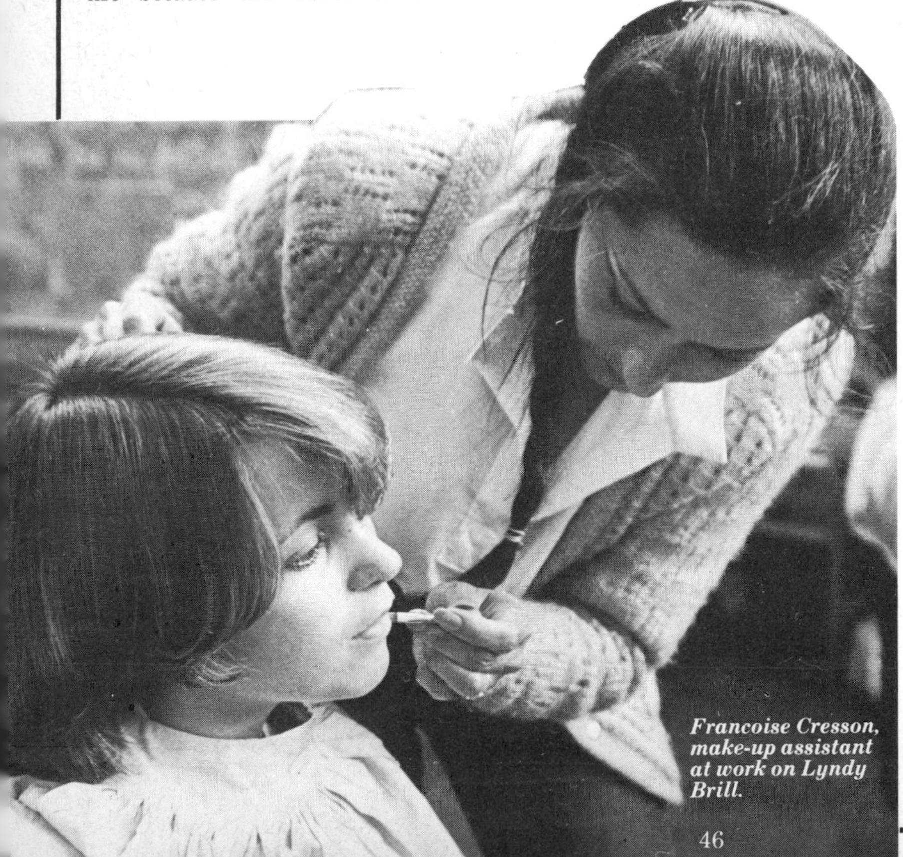

Francoise Cresson, make-up assistant at work on Lyndy Brill.

SWEATY

"Another part of my job is remembering whether someone is wearing

SCENES

Many people work very hard to make sure Grange Hill stays the way it is — great! We talked to two of them about their jobs ...

"The BBC does have a large stock wardrobe of clothes, but it's obviously very important to choose 'in' things — the type of clothes that are available in the shops now. My job involves quite a bit of leg work, just walking round the stores keeping in touch. I stick to the smaller, cheaper shops and usually find just what I'm looking for.

IRENE WHILTON
Costume Designer

"The one big problem with new clothes is that they look new. Outfits from our wardrobe usually appear quite tatty, so the new clothes have to be washed, dyed or bleached until they look the same. A school load of pupils walking around in immaculate clothes would look most unrealistic.

"Sometimes, I let a pupil break away from the guidelines. Children always try to push the rules and flaunt authority, so I'll deliberately get them to wear banned jewellery or the wrong type of heels.

"Most of the children are average sizes — but buying clothes for the tubbies or skinnies is no problem because most shops stocking clothes for teenagers are more than aware of the vast size differences and stock clothes to fit any shape.

FRESH

"My biggest headache is the rate at which the children grow. They're just at the age where sudden growth spurts are normal. They seemed to grow in front of our very eyes during the last series which meant a lot of work re-adjusting and buying new clothes for the present run.

"But that really is the only disadvantage. I really enjoy working on *Grange Hill*. I love everyone being so young and fresh and watching them grow — as people, as well as in body. It's refreshing and encouraging.

"And working with young people has given me a fresh look at them. I talk to them and get their opinion as I would to an adult actor. I wouldn't dream of talking down to them and because of this they respond well. It makes the job very worthwhile."

P.S. It's no good writing to the BBC to ask what happens to the outgrown clothes. Sadly, they're not available. They all go back into the stock cupboard.

a hair-slide and on which side it is. That's when those Polaroids come in so useful.

"Bruises are always fun. If there's any kind of fight scene within the series, the make-up team has to work very hard. We're all dab hands at black eyes. There was also one scene where one of the boys was drunk and we had to give him a sweaty forehead. That's quite difficult ..."

VARIED

As Maureen explained, her job is very varied indeed. She's worked for the BBC for some time and has been involved in many different series — a lot of them period costume dramas.

"That really is totally different. I'm first given the book to read. Then I have to study the period along with all the fashions, hairstyles and looks that the era produced. And all that — before I can even get started.

SPECIAL

"Because *Grange Hill* is bang up-to-date, a lot of that work was cut out. But it's just as demanding, even though the children are all very professional and know the routine back to front. They've each got their special times for coming in — before filming and inbetween scenes — and wait patiently to be checked. They're all very concerned that they should look the part — even down to the last straggly hair."

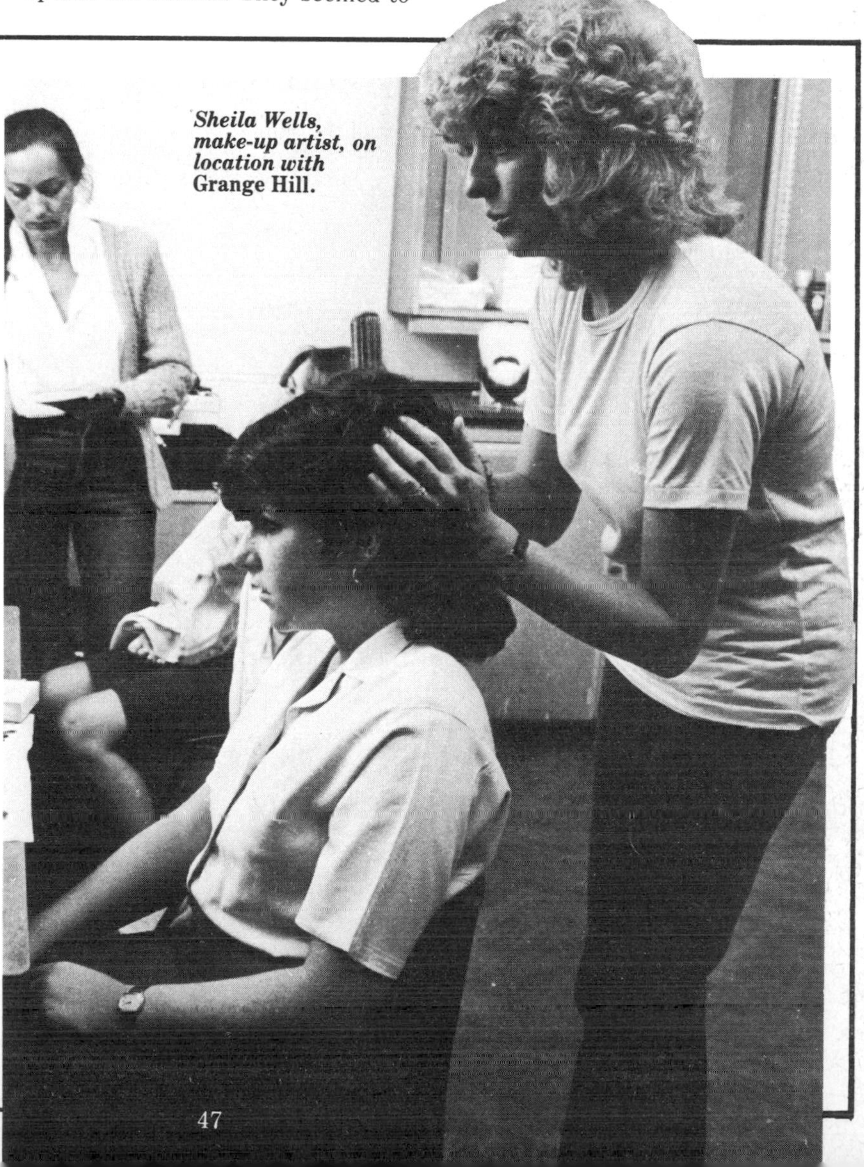

Sheila Wells, make-up artist, on location with **Grange Hill.**

Who's top of the form?

You don't have to be Mastermind to survive the average school day — all you need are a few brain cells and a bit of organisation. Find out here if you've got what it takes!

1. Phew — another hard day over! But what's the last thing you do before you leap into bed?
a) Check you've a clean blouse or shirt and that the clothes you wear to school are presentable?
b) Fall over the piles of junk lying on the floor waiting to be sorted out?
c) Remember your shoes need cleaning, and make a mental note to do it tomorrow?

2. Your history teacher has threatened to test you all on a certain subject in the next lesson. So do you ...
a) Try to cram as much into your brain as possible in the hour between tea and going out?
b) Study the subject as thoroughly as you always do. There won't be any catching you out?
c) Pack your books to take home, only to discover you've brought your maths ones by mistake. Looks like you'll have to bluff your way through it?

3. They've cast all the leading parts for the school play, but backstage help is desperately needed. Do you ...
a) Volunteer to be Stage Manager and throw yourself into the task with enthusiasm?
b) Hope to get a small part in the chorus. You're no good at backstage work?
c) You're too late to take a leading role and you're not practical enough to help out backstage, so you give the whole show a miss?

4. Before you can go on an end-of-term outing, your parents have to sign a form giving their permission. Do you ...
a) Keep forgetting to take the form home — and when you actually do remember, you forget to bring it back, so you miss out on the trip?
b) Remember to take it home the night before the deadline, so you make the outing by the skin of your teeth?
c) Make sure the form is pushed under their noses and signed as soon as poss, so you can return it to school and start looking forward to the outing?

5. On average, how many times a week do you make it to school before the first bell goes?
a) More often than not, you make it to registration — but hardly ever before the first bell?
b) You always make a point of being punctual?
c) You're usually there on time — or if you're late, it's the bus's fault?

6. Tuesday afternoon means double games, and once in the changing room you tip out your carrier bag to find ...
a) Your plimsolls and a cheese sandwich. You must have left the rest at home?
b) Your cookery/metalwork apron. Oops!?
c) Your games gear, of course, all freshly washed and neatly folded in a tidy pile?

SCORE

1.	a) 10	b) 0	c) 5
2.	a) 5	b) 10	c) 0
3.	a) 10	b) 0	c) 5
4.	a) 0	b) 5	c) 10
5.	a) 0	b) 10	c) 5
6.	a) 5	b) 0	c) 10

0-15: A bit helpless and scatter-brained, aren't you? We're surprised you even make it to school each day. Maybe if you stopped day-dreaming and tried to concentrate a bit more on what you're supposed to be doing, you wouldn't find school so much of a bother after all. Score 2/10 for giving the rest of us a laugh!

20-40: Although things occasionally go wrong for you, you're not going to stand out from the class as the fool with sawdust for brains. Most of the time you can muddle by without appearing either an organisational genius or a dummy. Score 6/10 for effort and memory. But try to be a bit more 'together'.

45-60: Go to the top of the class, clever clogs! You're the one who's never caught out. You like to arrange every detail of your own life, and other people's too, given half a chance. Mind they don't resent you for interfering or just for being right all the time, though! Score 10/10 (but don't let it go to your head!).

JAMES WYNN (MR. SUTCLIFFE)

BIRTHDAY: Unknown **STAR SIGN:** Unknown
HAIR: Fair **EYES:** Blue/grey **HEIGHT:** 6'2"
SISTERS: Unknown **BROTHERS:** Unknown **PETS:** Unknown
HOBBIES/INTERESTS: He likes to walk down the street pretending to be Bob Dylan or Bruce Springsteen!
MUSIC: Probably Bob Dylan and Bruce Springsteen!
AMBITION: Unknown **OTHER APPEARANCES:** James is a bit of a mystery character. No one knows very much about him at all! He has appeared in *Secret Army* though, and on stage in various places around Britain

No one could believe the news, but it was true. The Head had introduced Saturday detentions ...

Saturday Morning Fever!

IF Mr. Davey was mean with his physics marks, he made up for it by being extra-generous with his detentions. Only a small handful of his pupils had managed to avoid "the big D" during his lessons, and that was more through luck than good behaviour. A badly-timed cough, a sideways glance, a misdirected pellet or an atrocious piece of homework all earned the same punishment.

The fact that he had become something of a standing joke amongst the pupils at *Grange Hill* escaped his notice, though not that of his colleagues on the staff who had to put up with his considerable contributions to the nightly queues outside the detention room. They nicknamed detention duty "Davey-sitting".

It was Tucker Jenkins who held the record for the most detentions in a week. Fifteen was his proud boast, ten of them at the hands of Mr. Davey which meant, of course, that the rest of the staff didn't get much of a look in. And with bookings disappearing into the distant future, Tucker felt free to do more or less as he pleased in most lessons.

Not surprisingly, Tucker's form, G3, held the record for the most detentions received during a single period. That was 23, awarded during a particularly chaotic physics lesson in which Mr. Davey spent more time writing names in his detention book than actually teaching. But that suited most of the class.

However, G3's crown was in danger of slipping. Young pretenders to the throne were arriving on the scene, notably H1, with 19 detentions during one Davey session to their discredit. And Pogo Patterson, their undisputed champion had already chalked up his 50th detention that term. The fact that he couldn't possibly fit them all in was neither here nor there.

Matters came to a head — and ultimately to *the* Head — after a Thursday afternoon art class in which a tube of red paint with the cap removed somehow found its way on to Michael Doyle's chair, just as he sat down. Whether or not Tucker Jenkins was solely responsible, he accepted the blame.

Besides having to pay for the trousers being cleaned, he was given two hours' detention by a livid Miss Summers.

"Can't be this week, miss," he pouted, mock-apologetically, flicking through the pages of his notepad. "I'm booked solid." Pause for effect and the appreciative laughter of his classmates. "How about next Thursday and Friday? That suit ya all right?"

CHEEKY DEVIL

Ten minutes later, still speechless with rage, Miss Summers stormed into the staff room where, as luck would have it, she found Bill Davey checking his time-table.

"Something gone wrong?" he asked innocently.

"Hmph!" she snorted and plumped herself down at the opposite end of the room.

Spurned, Davey went back to his time-table. A couple of minutes later, Andrea Lexington walked in and threw herself down in a corner seat. Evidently, it wasn't a bed of roses in the maths department, either.

"That Douglas Patterson!" she hissed. "Really, I could wring his little neck at times. Do you know, I gave him a detention last lesson and the cheeky devil had the nerve to say he could fit it in sometime next month!"

"Funny you should have that problem, too..." said Miss Summers, calming down a bit. She described her troubles with a capital 'T', for Tucker, and as they got chatting, they came to the same conclusions. That detentions weren't effective as a form of punishment, mainly because too many were being handed out by one particular department, and one particular individual in it.

From the comments she'd heard around the staff room, it seemed to Andrea Lexington

A Grange Hill Story

that many teachers wanted the system revised. With Miss Summers to back her up, she decided to raise the matter at the next staff meeting.

If Bill Davey was listening or if any arrows found their target, it didn't show. Within the hour, he was back in class, detaining kids right, left and centre.

★★★★★★★★★★★

"Hey, heard the latest?" Cathy Hargreaves looked in the mirror as she combed her hair and saw Trisha Yates standing next to her, doing the same. "They want to introduce Saturday detentions."

"What? Who told you that?" Trisha gasped.

"Doyley's been spreading it around. Says he was snooping outside the staff room when they had that meeting the other day. Seems they've got to get the Governors' permission or something. And they're doing letters for us to take home to our parents. See what they think of the idea."

"Know what my mum'll think," Trisha murmured. "She'll tell 'em to get lost. She needs me to help with the shopping on Saturdays."

"It's only the mornings they're on about," Cathy explained as they clopped noisily down the stairs. "Not Saturday afternoons."

"Big deal. Anyway, what made them come up with a stupid idea like that? Whose brainwave was it?" Trisha's face screwed up with contempt as she took a seat in the cloakroom. Cathy leaned against the wall.

"Doyle says Miss Dawson suggested it. Said it worked in other schools she'd been at. Seems our lot are fed up doing detention duty at nights." She looked up as Penny Lewis and Pamela Cartwright joined them. They'd heard the rumours, too.

Their fears were confirmed that afternoon when sealed white envelopes were handed out, addressed to parents. The forms inside them, they were told, were to be read and completed before being returned to the school within the week.

Pogo Patterson had his envelope open before he had left the school premises. Huh, he thought, as he took in the contents of the letter. There's no way my dad'll vote for that.

Michael and Benny Green shared the same confidence as they walked home that night. Neither of them had dared to open his envelope. But they knew what they contained in any case.

"Think of the effect it might have on the school's soccer teams," Benny exclaimed. "There'd be nobody around to play on Saturday mornings."

"Should suit you okay, as long as you steer clear of trouble," his brother grinned.

"What do you mean?"

"Well...less competition for places. Only way you'll be sure of a place," he hooted, running off as Benny hurled his football at him.

"Anyway," said Benny when he'd caught up with him, "even if they do bring in Saturday detentions, sportsmen would be exempt, I expect." It was a comforting thought.

But their complacency was soon shattered when they reached home. To their horror, their parents' reactions to the letters were quite favourable ...

★★★★★★★★★★★

The following Wednesday, the votes having been counted, the Head called a special staff meeting after school to announce the result. Sensing that the ensuing debate was likely to be prolonged, it was announced that school would finish half an hour early that day which pleased most pupils but filled others with apprehension.

The issue had caused heated arguments in the staff room over the past week, straining old friendships and cementing old rivalries. Most teachers were in favour of experimenting with Saturday detentions, but a determined minority — the PE department plus a few others were immovably against it.

Consequently, when the Head arrived to begin the meeting, the staff were already aligned in rival factions, glowering at each other across the room.

The parents' overwhelming support for Saturday detentions was announced, and a report given of the meeting of school governors at which they had, after some deliberation, given their consent to the introduction of such detentions for a trial period. Then tempers came to the boil.

"Detentions ought to be abolished altogether!" Mr. Baxter wasn't afraid to speak his mind, especially when he knew he was speaking for his whole department. "They're completely unnecessary!"

The Head knew his feelings on the subject all too well and tried to calm him down.

"And what would you replace them with, Mr. Baxter?" the Head asked, silencing the hecklers.

"I've got my methods," he muttered.

"Yes, and we all know what they are, don't we," shouted Monica Dawson, stirring things. "But we can't all get away with using the plimsoll, can we!"

Her outburst signalled the start of some hysterical rantings aimed at the PE department, who according to some, seldom bothered to turn up for their spells of detention duty anyway. Miss Hugson, for girls' PE, countered by pointing out that working on a Saturday morning would be a new experience for most members of staff. Her department, however, regarded Saturday mornings as part of the normal working week as that was when most competitive games took place.

The squabbling rose to incredible heights of bitching before the Head intervened with a yell.

"Please...Please! Can we all stop behaving like children and start conducting this discussion like intelligent grown-ups?"

A ten minute truce followed during which the matter was put to the vote. The Head wanted to make sure of staff backing before introducing the new system.

POOR LOSER

A resounding cheer went up when it became instantly obvious that the motion had been carried.

"Well, tough luck, PE department!" someone cried. But they had the common sense to remain anonymous. Mr. Baxter was a poor loser.

"It's no skin off my nose!" he fumed as he made for the door. "Won't affect me, or my colleagues, in the slightest!"

And with that parting salvo, he promptly left.

"What did he mean by that?" Graham Sutcliffe asked Mr. Hopwood.

"Search me! Probably got some petty plan up his sleeve."

"Not at all," said Janet Hugson, following her leader. "He meant that none of us will be able to take Saturday morning detentions. We'll be too busy on the sports field!"

★★★★★★★★★★★

Within a few days, lists began to appear on notice boards, "reminding" wrong-doers that for the next month, their detentions would take place on Saturday mornings in rooms 10 and 11 where two members of staff would be in attendance.

"Can't see it making a blind bit

SATURDAY MORNING FEVER

of difference to the likes of Tucker," Tom Watson sniggered, seeing the name P. Jenkins on the list. "He's a natural for detentions. Almost hooked on 'em, he is."

Pamela Cartwright didn't agree. "Losing your Saturday morning is worse than losing the odd hour after school. I think it will make people behave themselves."

Suzanne Ross pointed out two other regulars on the list.

"You won't be seeing Duane on the football pitch this Saturday," she said to Claire Scott who stood nearby. "Just think, a whole morning without seeing him! How will you survive?"

"Huh," Claire sniffed, feeling sorry for Duane. "You won't be seeing Pogo Patterson, for that matter!"

"Oooh! What's this? A bit of scandal?" said Pamela Cartwright, eavesdropping. "You're not going out with Douglas Patterson, are you?"

Claire smiled to herself as she left Suzanne trying to squash the rumour before it became more than a joke.

As Saturday drew nearer, the PE department realised that the new system was going to affect them after all. But not how they thought. What happened was this. Whereas before, under the old system, teachers tended to be rather lenient towards detainees who could prove that they had to attend a netball match practice or a soccer training session, now that open war had been declared with the PE department, no mercy was shown. Pupils selected for the school teams were to be treated like all the rest and, perhaps, even deliberately picked on.

BACK DOWN

The result was that by Friday night, members of the PE staff were scurrying around trying to fix up replacements for the players who had received detentions. For some kids, like Richard Marks and Jimmy Leigh, last-minute selection was a dream come true. For others, like Alan Humphries, it was an imposition.

Bullet's first reaction, on hearing how the various teams had been decimated, was to march straight to the Head's room and demand the release of certain players. Those whom he felt had been victimised. But Mr. Sutcliffe, Miss Peterson, Mr. Mitchell and Mr. Davey felt it was impossible for them to back down at this late stage, so the Head had no alternative but to give them full support.

Like a demented bull, Baxter charged out of the study, cursing the day he'd come to teach at *Grange Hill*.

"Have you got us off it, sir?" asked Duane Orpington, dashing up to him and making things ten times worse. Half a dozen eager faces waited for the good news that Baxter couldn't give them.

"Blimey! Gorlington will flatten us tomorrow with half our team sitting stewing in here!" Duane protested.

No-one knew that better than Mr. Baxter. Gorlington could always be relied on to produce strong soccer teams. *Grange Hill* couldn't have chosen a worse week to field weakened sides.

"Poor Maureen's lost half a

Pogo Patterson had his envelope open before he had left the school premises ...

hockey team," Mr. Mitchell reported as Baxter entered his office. "It's hardly worth our while turning out tomorrow."

"We can't cancel," said Baxter. "Not this late. Not unless the weather turns bad."

Next morning was bright and sunny, offering not even the glimmer of an excuse for calling off the matches. As nine-thirty approached, cars started arriving outside the changing rooms and hordes of big, Gorlington lads poured from them, looking forward to some hard games. Baxter's hopes sank out of sight when he saw familiar faces in their line-ups. This lot'll run riot against our defence, he groaned.

As groups of *Grange Hill* lads arrived, he hurried them into the changing rooms, trying to sound as keen and confident as ever. Once inside, he delivered his pre-match pep talk with the usual verve, knowing all the while that it was a miracle they'd be needing out there on the pitch.

In the room next door, Mr. Mitchell was introducing the members of his first year team to each other, while a couple of miles away, at Gorlington's playing fields, Mr. Foster was trying to sort out kit problems with his makeshift team of second years.

The girls' hockey teams, playing against Brookfield, were in a sorry state, too. The third year team consisted of a mixture of second and third year girls, while the second year team had only nine players.

Cathy Hargreaves grinned at Trisha Yates as they changed.

"Betcha we go and stuff 'em ten nil," she chuckled. "That's the sort of thing that happens at times like this!"

★★★★★★★★★★★

About the same time that the others were changing, their missing team-mates were waiting outside rooms 10 and 11 for the duty teachers to show up. Mr. Sutcliffe and Mrs. Kennedy had been given the dubious honour of supervising *Grange Hill's* first Saturday morning detentions.

"Hear about Davey Crockett?" Tucker said to Pogo Patterson and Duane Orpington who were sitting next to him. Duane wasn't interested. He'd rather have been out playing football right now. "He set a new record this week. Gave a whole football team detention!"

"Not a whole team, strictly speaking," Pogo noted. He was a stickler for accuracy on such matters. "Eleven players, from different teams."

"Oh, all right then," admitted Tucker. He hated nitpickers. "But it was still the equivalent of a whole team."

"Okay, you horrible lot," barked Mr. Sutcliffe, unusually cheerful considering he was working an extra half day. "Let's get on with it!" And he marched them all into the room for his first and last spell of duty that term.

★★★★★★★★★★★

"Good game, Freddie," Mr. Baxter said sympathetically, ruffling his goalkeeper's hair as he slunk past. "Couldn't blame you for the result. You saved at least six certs there." He didn't mention the eight that went right past him.

"Things would have been different if we'd fielded a full-strength team," predicted Benny Green as he came off the pitch alongside the smug Gorlington captain.

"Excuses! Should go to a decent school, shouldn't you." They parted company at the changing room doors. "One that doesn't have stupid Saturday detentions — like Gorlington!"

SENT OFF

"Hah! Gorlington!" Benny snorted. "Hey, how'd you get on?" he asked Richard Marks who was first back from the other game.

"Lost 7-1," he mumbled. "How about you?"

"8-0." The look on Benny's face told Richard not to ask whether that was for or against.

On Monday morning, the full extent of the weekend's humiliation became known. On top of those two tankings, both girls' hockey teams went down by record scores. The second year team emerged with some credit, achieving a 0-0 draw, but that was due to two opponents being sent off in the first half.

SATURDAY MORNING FEVER

Mr. Baxter protested to the Head, of course, but didn't expect and didn't get any satisfaction. He stormed out of the study to face the sly smiles and taunts of the academic staff.

The next two Saturdays proved equally hard for him to endure. The same names cropped up on the detention lists, despite warnings from him and his PE colleagues that they had just better not. For a second and then a third time, *Grange Hill* fielded weakened teams and suffered for it.

"I've had enough of this!" Baxter hissed, after the third series of massacres. "It's making a mockery of our jobs!"

First thing on Monday morning, Baxter and his colleagues in the PE department were outside the Head's study, demanding an audience. Tommy Watson and Alan Humphries saw them go in.

"Blimey!" Alan chortled. "Bullet's got murder in his eyes!"

Inside the Head's study, Mr. Baxter delivered his ultimatum. Unless something was done about these detentions, either by exempting those selected for school teams or by arranging alternative times for such people to attend, then he and his colleagues would refuse to take games on a Saturday.

"Well, I'll have to think about it, Mr. Baxter," the Head said, seeing that there was no way of soft-soaping them. "But I can't promise anything."

The door closed firmly behind them as they left the room. "Oh, dear," the Head sighed, getting up and pacing across the room. "What have we got ourselves into now?"

"Well, I must say that they had a valid complaint," said Mr. Keating who had remained behind.

The Head turned and looked at him, rather shocked.

"Surely, you're not suggesting that we should turn a blind eye to the misbehaviour of those pupils who are athletic enough to be chosen for the school teams!"

WAY OUT

"Not at all," he tutted, raising his hands in mock horror. "No, no, they must be treated like all the others." He strolled across to the bookshelf and stared at the titles. "What I am trying to say is that perhaps it is not only the behaviour of the pupils which should come under scrutiny."

"Do you know something that I don't?"

"Well…I gather that a certain member of staff may be largely to blame for the parents' dissatisfaction with weekday detentions. And, I might add, the growing disillusionment with the present system." He could see it was all startling news.

The Head was about to ask him for the identity of the person when he silenced the remark by going on.

"Now, I know that we prefer to sort out our own little problems, whenever possible. No big stick and all that. So would it be in order for me to suggest a way out of all our present difficulties?"

★★★★★★★★★★★

Two days later, another note was circularised to all parents. It informed them that, due to unforeseen circumstances, the school had decided not to continue with Saturday detentions after that weekend, when the trial period ended. Weekday detentions would resume as before, although there would be certain administrative changes which would not concern them directly.

Even before he'd sneaked a look at his copy of the letter, Tucker had latched on to what was happening. For the first time in months, he had emerged from a Davey session without a detention.

"It's obvious what they're gonna do," he said to Tommy and Alan, amazed that anyone could be so thick. "I'll lay odds that teachers are being asked to take their own detentions."

If anyone had been fool enough to take his bet, they'd have lost, for that very afternoon they were put in the picture by Miss Peterson. From now on, anyone who gave detentions had to stay behind and supervise them in their own classrooms.

"Shame, really," Tucker grinned, chewing gum. "I was taking bookings for next year and all!"

"Tucker Jenkins! Come out here and spit that disgusting lump of chewing gum in the bin!" Tucker did. "And I'll see you in here tomorrow at 3.30."

"Flippin' heck!" he groaned. "Here we go again!"

THE END

Pupils selected for the school teams were to be treated like all the rest!

Grange Hill

VINCENT HALL (DOYLE)

BIRTHDAY: 5th August, 1963 **STAR SIGN:** Leo
HAIR: Brown **EYES:** Blue **HEIGHT:** Unknown
SISTERS: None **BROTHERS:** 1 aged 19 **PETS:** 1 dog and 2 cats called Tiger and Lucky
HOBBIES/INTERESTS: Skating, swimming and horse-riding
MUSIC: Likes most kinds of pop music
AMBITION: Not known **OTHER APPEARANCES:** Vince has been in quite a few programmes and shows, but most recently *The Eagle Has Landed* (film) with Michael Caine. He has also appeared with Roger Moore

Find out who gets called what!

THE NAME GAME!

Everyone's got a nickname — some are funny, some are nasty and some are just plain strange! We asked a few pop people about names they were called at school!

LEO NEVER SUFFERED!

"I can't remember having any nickname when I was at school — or at art college after that," Leo Sayer told us, "but I do remember one of my friend's silly names!

"His nickname was 'Legweak'! I know it's a strange one — it's one of those clever ones that you have to sit down and try and work out. It was because his surname was Armstrong!"

BIG MOUTH BOB!

"I suppose my mouth is quite large," Bob Geldof of The Boomtown Rats confessed, "but I still reckon the people at my school were a bit cruel calling me 'Liver Lips'!

"They used to make jokes about my mum wetting my lips and sticking me to the window when she went into the supermarket to get the shopping!"

SNOWY'S ALL WHITE!

"I've been called Snowy White ever since I can remember," the guitarist with Thin Lizzy smiled.

"I don't think it's anything to do with the seven dwarfs, although I suppose that's where it originally came from! I've never told anybody my real name, and I don't think my mum and dad can remember, either! They always call me Snowy!"

THE TRUTH ABOUT TUCKER JENKINS!

Ever wondered why Peter Jenkins is called Tucker? Well, we're afraid that nobody knows! He's been called Tucker for so long that even he has forgotten!

As for Pogo Patterson, that's obvious! His dad bought him a pogo stick once and Pogo broke it on the first bounce!

THE TOURISTS HAD A TOUGH TIME!

Eddie Chin and Jim Toomey from The Tourists have no trouble remembering their nicknames!

"They used to call me Double at school," Eddie told us. "You know, Double Chin — get it?" Sounds a bit mean to us!

"I had to suffer two nicknames," Jim remembers, "I used to be called 'Do It' by my mates 'cos I was full of energy and ready to do anything. No sooner was it said than I was ready to get it done! And when I was playing up in class, one teacher especially used to have great pleasure in calling me to the front of the class by saying, "Toomey, come to me!"

Grange Hill

PAULA ANN BLAND (CLAIRE SCOTT)

BIRTHDAY: 23rd May, 1968 **STAR SIGN:** Gemini
HAIR: Blonde **EYES:** Blue **HEIGHT:** Unknown
SISTERS: None **BROTHERS:** None **PETS:** Goldfish called Kelly
HOBBIES/INTERESTS: Likes singing, dancing and going out with all her friends **AMBITION:** She'd like to carry on acting and appear in a musical film one day
OTHER APPEARANCES: Paula has appeared in quite a few commercials and also attended some charity shows. She really enjoys her part in *Grange Hill* and has made lots of friends in the cast

A range Hill Story

Who's Bunking Off?

The last person Duane wanted to see was Mr. Sutcliffe, but there he was, as large as life ...

His mind was a mess of ifs and buts, likelihoods and total improbabilities!

"SHORTEST one goes." Pogo Patterson held out a plump fist with several strips of white paper sticking up out of it. Some were taller than others. Tactics, thought Duane Orpington, giving the fist two hundred percent attention. After all, it would decide where he was to spend tomorrow morning.

"Hurry up! Take one before I go down with cramp!"

Duane refused to be hurried. This needed a bit of thinking out. It was pretty certain Pogo didn't want him to pick one of the taller pieces; that was why he'd made them stick up so much. On the other hand, it might be a double bluff...

"If you don't pick one soon, I will." Pogo was annoyed. Too much deduction by the Orpington brainbox — or what passed as one — and he might find himself lumbered. Besides, it was getting cold. Much longer and his fist would be frozen solid.

Slowly, cautiously, Duane's hand moved towards the bits of paper, hovered for a second and then descended in a series of jerks to pluck one from Pogo's grasp. His mind was a mess of ifs and buts, likelihoods and improbabilities, bluffs, double bluffs and treble bluffs. What the hell, he decided. He'd have to take pot luck.

"Unlucky!" grinned Pogo, with unconcealed relief. He opened the palm of his hand and spread the remaining strips across it to show their respective lengths. "You picked the shortest one straight off!"

"Lemme see!" Duane grabbed the hand before it could clamp shut on the evidence.

Slowly, he ran his scrap of paper along the row, comparing, measuring, hoping against hope.

"Believe me now?" Pogo crowed after the result had been confirmed. He caught a glimpse of the Deputy Head chasing stragglers indoors. "Hey, come on, we're late!"

"Why's it always me?" Duane moaned, thumping the swing doors open harder than was necessary. "I went last time, when we were drawn against Wolves in the Cup."

"Well, you'll know where the tickets are sold then."

"Oi!" The voice of officialdom stopped them in their tracks. "Where do you think you two are going?"

They wheeled round to find Mr. Thomson, the caretaker, watching them, hands on hips.

"To our next lesson."

"And pray what does this

arrow on the wall indicate?" He pointed poker-faced to a sign above his head.

"The longest way to get there!"

"None of your lip, sonny! It indicates the new one-way system, designed to make all our lives a bit easier."

"But our room's that way..."

"No arguing! Off you go!"

"Stupid one-way system," Pogo muttered as they headed off in the opposite direction from their lesson. "I can understand it when the corridors are packed, but not when there's only us!"

★★★★★★★★★★★

It wasn't Andrea Lexington's day. She realised that when she arrived in her classroom to find her cushion missing, the light over the blackboard fused and workmen drilling in the room next door. On top of all that, she had HI to contend with for a double lesson.

"Oooh!" she tutted in frustration as she snapped her third piece of chalk in as many minutes. The drill drowned out the giggles which she knew were going on behind her back.

Keeping the book she was copying from open in one hand,

WHO'S BUNKING OFF?

she knelt to pick up the broken piece of chalk. Predictably, on such a day, several stitches went in her denim skirt, loudly enough for the two front rows to hear, despite the background noise.

She stood bolt upright, a hand trying to detect the damage, her face as red as her fingernails.

As if on cue, the door opened and in walked Duane Orpington and Douglas Patterson.

"Hey, what's the joke?" Pogo asked Matthew Cartwright who was in fits. Others had tears streaming down their cheeks.

"Where have you two been?" Miss Lexington was glad of anything that would divert attention away from her private misfortune. She pointed to the clock. It vibrated quite clearly. Any second, she expected the point of a drill to come bursting through its face. "Do you realise half a lesson has gone?"

"Got lost in the one-way system, miss," Duane shrugged, raising his voice to compete with the bionic dentist. He didn't sound convincing, even though he was telling the truth.

"You mean to say you've spent nearly fifteen minutes wandering around totally lost in your own school!"

"Yes, miss."

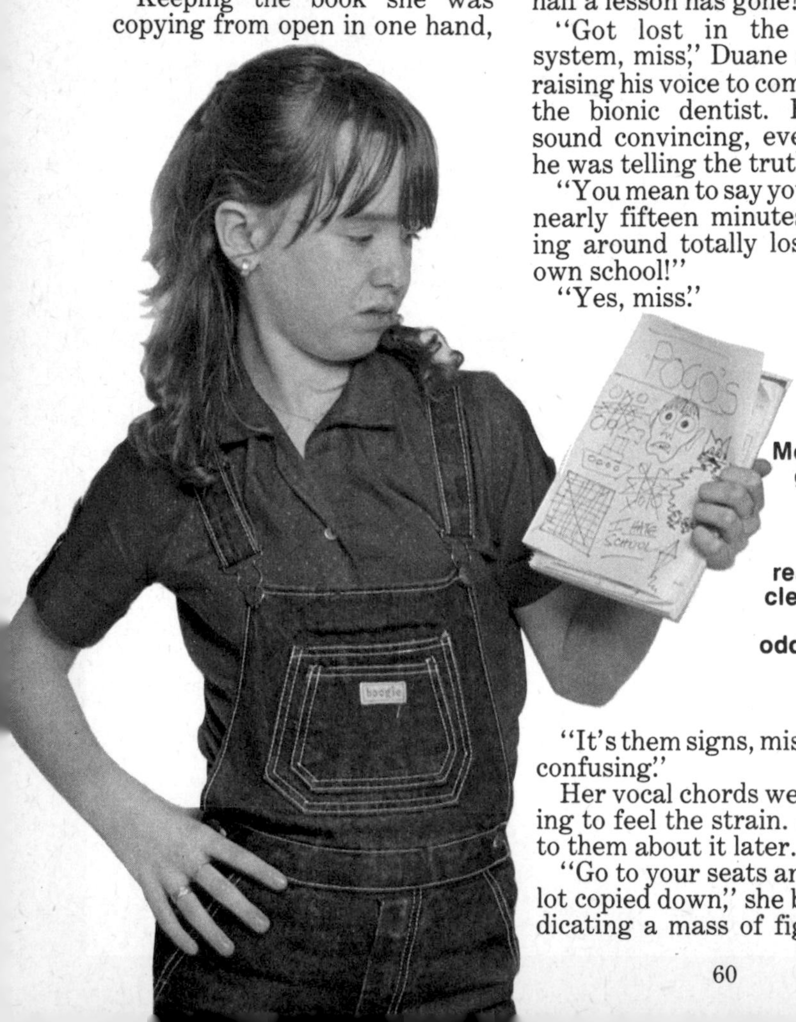

Most of the girls kept their exercise books reasonably clean, apart from the odd stick-on flower.

"It's them signs, miss. They're confusing."

Her vocal chords were beginning to feel the strain. She'd talk to them about it later.

"Go to your seats and get that lot copied down," she barked, indicating a mass of figures that made Einstein's equations look like the one times table.

"Miss," piped up Christopher Stewart at the front. He waved a dog-eared once-orange jotter at her. "My book's full. Can I have a new one?"

She groaned and took some sheets of graph paper from a drawer. "I'm out of new exercise books, Christopher. You'll have to make do with this for the time being." She handed the paper to him.

With any luck, the wall would cave in before the lesson was through.

NO REPLY

"Has everyone finished that exercise?" asked Graham Sutcliffe, looking up from the notes he was making. They were needed for the next period and this substitution hadn't helped.

"Yeah, we finished it last term," muttered Cathy Hargreaves to Trisha Yates as she closed the maths book they were sharing.

"I tried telling him that," said Trisha, "but he wouldn't listen."

Cathy dumped their copy of the New Advanced Mathematics, Book 3 on Sutcliffe's desk as they left.

"When's Mr. Sim coming back, sir?" she enquired.

"I don't know, Cathy. As soon as possible, I hope."

"What's wrong with him?" said Trisha, trying to read what was on the desk. Anything to delay going to French.

All she got in reply was a shrug.

Wouldn't we all like to know the answer to that one, Sutcliffe sighed as he gathered his papers together. Clive Sim was a puzzle. One minute he was full of the joys of life; the next minute he was as depressing as a Peter Jenkins essay. A split personality, without doubt. Sutcliffe just wished that one of him would turn up to take his own lessons.

"Hello," a voice croaked from the door. "What brings you to the maths department?"

The sight of Andrea Lexington brightened his day. How could anyone look so good in just a sweater and a denim skirt?

"Substituting for Clive Sim," he explained as he prepared to leave. "No doubt inflicting G3 with some maths exercise that they've already done."

"Well, how are you to know what stage they're at? As long as you give them something to do," she smiled, opening the stock cupboard.

He paused to pick up something she'd put on the table nearby.

"Don't tell me this is someone's exercise book!" he gasped.

She emerged from the cupboard with a pack of new books. He sounded shocked.

"Yes," she said, moving to take it from him. "It's Christopher Stewart's. Why?"

"Why!" he spluttered, amazed by her apparent indifference. "Just look at the state it's in! Doodles all over the cover, and stickers! And feel the thickness of it. I'll bet it's only got half the number of pages it should have."

She snatched it from him. What business was it of his? Let him worry about his own department.

"As long as he does his work, I'm satisfied. It's what goes into an exercise book that's important," she snapped.

"But, Andrea... can't you see? The Head throws a fit about books in that state! I'm only trying to warn you."

"Thanks. I appreciate your concern." She left him standing in the doorway and marched off without looking back.

"Tell the little blighters to put covers on them. That's what I do!" he called after her.

★★★★★★★★★★

By 3.30, Christopher Stewart's popularity rating had sunk to zero. Just as HI was about to be dismissed, their maths books arrived by messenger from Miss Lexington with instructions to get them covered by the next lesson.

The girls were especially put out by it. Most of them — Sandra Dodding being the exception — kept their exercise books reasonably clean, apart from the odd stick-on flower or pin-up. Now they were being made to suffer because of Stewpot Stewart's untidyness.

"Enjoy giving other people work, do you?" sniffed Suzanne Ross as she pushed past him in the playground. "Some of us have better things to do with our time than to cover exercise

"This must've had last month's fish and chips in it," said Suzanne Ross.

books." But already she knew that her dad would offer to do hers for her.

GIRLS' STUFF

Stewpot ignored her. He'd already taken enough stick from his mates. The moaning stage having passed, they were now resigned to getting the job done.

"My dad's got some spare wallpaper left over. I'll nab some of that," Matthew Cartwright declared, pleased to think that was his problem solved.

"Wouldn't catch me putting daft wallpaper on my book," Pogo sneered. "That's girls' stuff. I know what I'm going to use on mine."

"What about you, Marksy? Got any paper in your house?" asked Duane, half joking, half serious. He knew how hard-up Richard Mark's family were.

"Might pinch some Christmas wrapping paper," he replied, knowing how scarce that was at home. He'd be lucky to get a present, never mind having it done up in fancy wrapping.

"I'm using newspaper," Pogo announced. "Plenty of that around. You can read it, too, during lessons!"

With that, the small group began to split up. Matthew and Stewpot joined the bus queue; Richard took the lane leading to the council estate; and Pogo and Duane were left plotting.

"Don't worry, I'll cover for you at lessons," Pogo assured his worried accomplice. "And if you get the chance of more tickets, grab them. We can sell them at twice the price on the day!"

"Oh, yeah? Where do I get the extra money from to buy them? You coughing up?"

Pogo kept quiet. He'd hoped Duane might have some spare loot stashed away. That was one snag with being a ticket tout. You had to lash out before you could rake it in.

"I'll come round tomorrow night. See how you got on," he said, leaving Duane at his gate. "Don't sleep in! And don't lose my money! I'll hold you responsible. And..."

Duane shut the door on Pogo's afterthoughts. If he was that worried, why didn't he go for the tickets himself?

He looked at his Spurs scarf hanging on the peg. He wished they'd put tickets for these games on sale in the evening instead of first thing in the morning. The trouble was, by night they'd all have gone. A local derby always attracted a big crowd. Especially with the two teams placed third and fourth in the league. That's why it was all-ticket. Going to school and missing out on it was out of the question.

★★★★★★★★★★

Miss Lexington was clearly amazed. Everyone in HI had

remembered to cover their exercise books, even though some of them had taken a malicious delight in the materials used.

"No Duane Orpington this morning?" she asked, seeing the empty seat.

"He's off ill, miss."

"Nothing serious, I trust?"

"Dunno, miss. Think it's stomach ache. Should be back tomorrow."

"Twenty-four hour stomach ache, is it, Douglas?" she sharply observed.

"Dunno, miss. Saw his mum when I passed his house." Her sarcasm was lost on him.

NO DOUBT

"Well, I hope you handed in the note which she no doubt gave you to bring in."

The colour drained from his ample cheeks. He hadn't thought of that!

Fortunately for Duane, if not for Pogo, Miss Lexington's attention was distracted by one particular exercise book which she picked up with real distaste. She wiggled a finger in Pogo's direction.

"Come here, young man!"

"Me, miss?" said Pogo, knowing full well what it was about.

Heads looked up from desks as the heavyweight of HI waddled to the front.

"What do you call that?" she said, holding up his book which had a nude girl on the cover.

"An exercise book. I covered it, like you said." He tried not to smile.

"That, Douglas, is not what I consider a proper cover. That, is pornography!"

"What's that, miss?" he enquired innocently. Laughter erupted behind him.

"Look it up in your dictionary. And then remove this young lady from the cover of your book and replace her with a decent cover."

"But you *said* we could use newspaper!" he pleaded.

"Not that particular page!"

Already, nosey parkers had left their desks and were crowding round Pogo to get a good look.

"Back to your seats, this minute," came the order. But it took rather longer for them to obey.

"Uggh! Smell that," shuddered Suzanne Ross, holding up another book swathed in stained newspaper. "Must've had last month's fish and chips in it!"

"Put it back!" shouted Richard Marks, grabbing it from her hand.

"Will you please sit down!" howled the demented teacher. But she needn't have bothered. The bell went for the next lesson.

★★★★★★★★★★★

Rain was gusting along the street as Duane took his place in the queue behind the North Stand. Twenty or thirty people had beaten him to it. He leaned against the wall and checked his cash. Fancy coming all this way and finding you were a penny short!

He'd left home as usual that morning, so as not to raise his mum's suspicions. As far as she knew, he was at school. He'd fill in the rest of the day down the High Street, the part she never visited.

WHO'S BUNKING OFF?

He glanced at his watch. Ten minutes to go until the ticket office opened. The queue was growing all the time. He pitied the poor beggars who arrived too late and didn't get a ticket after queuing that long.

"Orpington!" The mention of his name made him jump. "What are you doing here?"

He looked round to see Mr. Sutcliffe glaring at him from further down the line. Several swift strides later, he was standing over him.

"Why aren't you at school? Come on, answer me!"

"Dunno, sir," was all he could manage to say.

"You don't know! Well *I* know, lad! You're playing truant, that's what you're doing! Aren't you! Go on, admit it!"

"Yes, sir!" Duane felt like crawling into a hole. He knew everyone's eyes were watching him closely.

"Pity for you I had the morning off, otherwise you'd have got away with it, wouldn't you!" The veins stood out on Sutcliffe's neck. Duane had never seen him so angry. "Does your mother know you're here instead of in class?" Silence. "I bet she doesn't. But she will! Oh, yes. And just wait till I get you back in school!"

Duane couldn't stand much more. He turned to go.

"Where are you going?"

"School, sir." The prospect horrified him. How did you explain suddenly turning up after you'd told everyone you were ill?

"Didn't you come here for tickets?"

"Yes, sir!"

"Well, since you're already here, you might as well collect them."

"Thank you, sir," Duane murmured, rejoining the queue ...

★★★★★★★★★★★

Pogo looked like he'd seen a ghost when Duane appeared at break.

"What are you doing back here?" he gasped. "Got brain damage or something? You're not supposed to be back till tomorrow."

"Well, I'm back now," Duane shrugged. He'd resigned himself to taking his punishment. It hadn't occurred to him before that Pogo would get his share, too, for covering for him. "Bumped into Sooty, didn't I, right outside the ground. Gave me a right earful."

"Blimey!" The full horror of the situation took a minute to sink in. He was done for. They both were.

Duane waved a hand in the air and forced a smile to his face.

"Still got the tickets, though, didn't I!"

"Oh...great," said Pogo, glad they weren't stand seats. He couldn't see himself being able to sit down for a week after his dad got hold of him.

★★★★★★★★★★★

Remarkably, Duane's presence in class didn't raise any eyebrows until after lunch. Up to then, HI's timetable steered him clear of those teachers who had already noted his absence. He even began to think that he might get through the rest of the day without a nasty confrontation. Even planned where he'd hide for the last ten minutes when they had to return to their register class.

Duane waved a hand in the air and forced a smile on his face. "Still, I got the tickets!"

But, as so often happens, just when his hopes were highest, he ran right slap bang into Miss Lexington.

"Duane Orpington?" she called out as he did an abrupt about turn. "What are you doing in school?"

She stared at him until he had to look away.

"I was told you were ill."

"I was, miss," he stammered. Gotta take this slowly, he thought, before I say something wrong. "But I felt a bit better so I came in."

"Hmm. Very commendable. Chest pains gone?" she asked, setting her snare.

"Uh?...Oh...Yes!" he nodded, walking straight into it. Trust Pogo, he fumed. After they'd agreed it should be stomach ache.

"I think you'd better come and see me after school," she frowned. "And bring Douglas Patterson with you."

She turned to go and then remembered something.

"Oh...and Duane. Now that you are here — your exercise book, please." She held out a hand.

Duane looked puzzled.

"I asked you to have it covered for today's lesson."

"Forgot, miss!" His face creased up in a really pained expression.

"Not in more trouble, is he, Miss Lexington?" Graham Sutcliffe strode towards them. "He's up to his neck in it already, aren't you, Orpington!" Duane studied the floor. "What's he done this time?"

Miss Lexington was reluctant to tell him, but Duane took her silence to mean that he had to explain himself.

"Haven't covered my exercise book, sir," he mumbled.

Sutcliffe held back a smile. So she'd taken his advice after all. Well, he wouldn't rub it in. Better give her all his support.

"Why not?" he snapped.

"Forgot, sir."

"Nonsense. You just didn't bother." He looked at Miss Lexington. Her cheeks were glowing slightly. "How long has he had to do it?"

"He had all last night... but, of course, he was off school this morning."

"Yes, I know all about that, don't I, Orpington. Caught him playing truant," he explained.

Duane was ashamed to be proved a liar in front of Miss Lexington, of all people. She feigned surprise, although she'd already guessed something of the kind.

STERN LOOK

"However, I'm leaving the Head to deal with that," Sutcliffe went on. "From now on, though, I'm keeping a special watch on you, Orpington." He looked from him to her. "Tell me if he hasn't got that book covered by tomorrow, will you, and I'll deal with him personally."

She gave Duane a stern look. "You heard, Duane. Now, off you go."

Duane slunk off along the corridor, like a child being sent to bed with no supper. He heard his teachers still talking together as he left.

"Thanks, Graham," Miss Lexington said. "But I could have handled it myself. Anyway ... how'd you get on this morning?"

"This morning?"

"At the dentist's? Stuart said you'd an appointment."

"Oh...yes. Had a couple of fillings, that's all." Sutcliffe glanced nervously along the corridor, hoping Orpington had gone, but there he was, looking back at them. He must have heard every word. "Go on, Orpington!" he cried, angry at being found out.

"Look...er...about these exercise books," he said ponderously, reviewing the situation in his mind as he accompanied Andrea past the duplicating room, "perhaps you'd better give it a day or two before you call me in! Wouldn't do to undermine your authority, would it?"

Duane sneaked a look round a corner and watched them go. So much for Sooty's morning off, he thought. Still, it'd make things a bit easier when he had to apologise about his English homework...

THE END

Grange Hill

PAUL McCARTHY (TOMMY WATSON)

BIRTHDAY: 21st October, 1964 **STAR SIGN:** Libra
HAIR: Blond **EYES:** Blue **HEIGHT:** 5'8"
SISTERS: 2 older **BROTHERS:** 2 older **PETS:** A dog called Dodger who he often takes for walks
HOBBIES/INTERESTS: Roller-skating and girls **MUSIC:** All modern
AMBITION: Would like to work in America
OTHER APPEARANCES: Paul's had parts in *Mixed Blessings* (LWT), *Headmaster* (BBC), *Z Cars* (BBC), *The Black Panther* (film) and also played the Artful Dodger in a stage musical

Everyone at school has to go through...

A TESTING TIME!

What's the point in passing exams? Certificates are just worthless bits of paper, aren't they?

Some people say that passing exams is all a matter of luck. They reckon that all good results prove is that you're good at revising, have a clear memory and struck lucky on the questions asked.

And in some cases they're right. But that's not how future employers see exams. They want to know that you're the right sort of person to work for them. And if you've taken your studies seriously enough to pass exams — you're probably the kind of person, they consider, to take your job seriously.

Also, even if you are exceptionally lucky with the questions, you couldn't answer them if you didn't have an all-round knowledge of the subject. Most questions are worded very carefully to make sure you really do understand what you've been studying. Examiners know all the tricks and can tell when they're being fobbed off by long, flowery sentences that say nothing.

GOOD IDEA

It is, of course, dreadful luck if you've spent many hours studying one set of notes on say agriculture in Peru, only to find out when it comes to the exam that there's not one single question about it. But if you listen to your teachers and take their advice, that shouldn't happen. They don't know *exactly* what you're going to be asked, but they will have a pretty good idea. So ask them what you need to polish up on.

And when it comes to revision, don't leave it all until the last minute. It's boring — but if you set aside a certain number of hours a week specifically for revision, you're far more likely to have successful results than the person reading through their notes five minutes before the exam is due to start. If you can revise with a mate, so much the better. And don't forget to give yourself some time off occasionally. You do need the break.

The exams you take will depend upon your particular school. But it's likely they'll fall into one of the following categories.

C.S.E. (Certificate of Secondary Education)
C.S.E.'s are designed for pupils of average ability and take into account classroom work over the years as well as an exam result. A grade one pass is often regarded as the equivalent of an O-level. Taken at 16.

G.C.E. (General Certificate of Education)
G.C.E.'s cover an extremely wide range of subjects. O-level certificate exams (meaning ordinary level) are usually taken in the summer of the fifth year. A-levels (advanced levels) are taken two years later. S-levels may be taken by certain A-level candidates to test their knowledge at an even more advanced level. The S stands for Special. (And you need to be specially clever.)

Those are the most common exams, but you may also be allowed to sit for others including:

Pitmans (A test of secretarial skills including shorthand and also typing).

R.S.A. (Royal Society of Arts — sometimes taken before C.S.E. or G.C.E.'s).

And, unfortunately, the dreaded end of term exams which influence the report your parents receive.

The important thing about exams is not to worry about them. Some people are terrified of them. They go to pieces through nerves and feel physically sick as soon as they see an exam paper. This isn't very common though and in most cases, if you're prepared to work harder next time, you can always sit them again. If you don't want to stay on at school, try to get accepted at a technical college.

DON'T WORRY

At some stage or another, it's going to seem like the studying and the exams will go on forever. But try not to get depressed. They're only a very small part of your life and successful results can make all the difference.

Finally, in the unlikely event that you want to take an exam but your teacher won't let you, there's nothing you can do to force the issue. But you may be able to take it if you pay the entrance fee (usually paid by the school) yourself. Even then the Head and the examining board must agree.

Is Grange Hill *based on* Phil Redmond's

'My Liverpool school'

THE GRANGE HILL INTERVIEW

PHIL Redmond will never forget the first day at his new school. It wasn't even built!

"It was like going to school on a building site," he remembers. "There was me, looking all smart in my new cap and blazer, and the first thing I saw was a group of boys burning rubbish in the playground.

"Lessons were held in what later came to be the school dining halls. They were partitioned into three, but even then you could still hear everything that was going on. It was pretty hard to concentrate. Not that it took much to distract me, anyway."

Phil's school was one of the first comprehensives in the country. Back in 1960, when he passed his 11-plus, they were very much in the early experimental stages. He was supposed to have gone to his local grammar school, but something happened to change those plans. "My mum had a letter from the local authorities saying that I and a number of other grammar-school-bound lads had been chosen to go to this brand new mixed-ability paradise.

"My parents agreed that it was a good idea and I had to take a bus to the school which was fifteen miles away. I suppose me and my mates were guinea pigs in a way."

'I hated wearing school uniform'

The similarity between the fictional *Grange Hill Comprehensive* and Phil's own school in Kirkby, just outside Liverpool, is non-existent, however.

"There's no comparison at all," he told us. "There were three separate streams for a start — grammar, technical and secondary. It was just like having three different schools under one roof. Not a bit like *Grange Hill*. There weren't any girls at my school, either. I think that was wrong and I don't agree with single-sex schools. Society isn't split up into boys and girls — so why should school be like that?

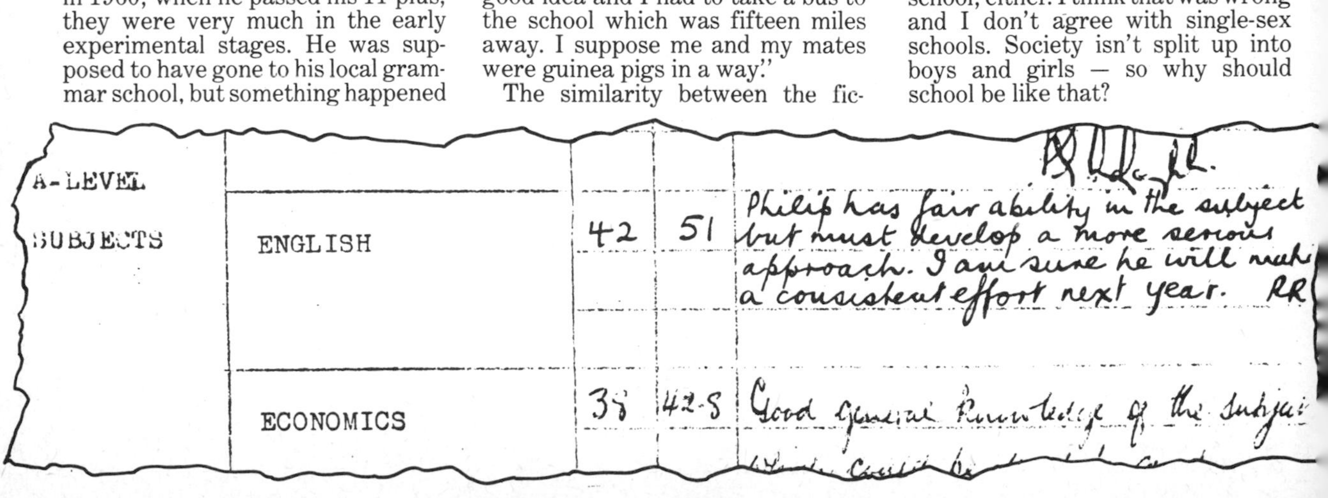

A-LEVEL SUBJECTS	ENGLISH	42	51	Philip has fair ability in the subject but must develop a more serious approach. I am sure he will make a consistent effort next year. RR
	ECONOMICS	38	42·5	Good general knowledge of the subject [illegible]

old school? Read on and find out...

"But going to a comprehensive has helped a lot with the series. For a start, because it was so large, I know how big schools work. And, though I'm not saying which on the grounds of incrimination, some of the characters resemble my old mates."

Again, unlike *Grange Hill*, uniform was compulsory for Phil until the sixth year.

"I hated wearing it. I felt so stupid. The caps were the worst thing. If they didn't end up in the river on the first day, they were folded in half and used as weapons to belt people round the head.

"Considering that there were

'We always chose the strap'

2,500 boys in the school, there weren't that many fights. I'm not saying it wasn't rough, though. There was another school next to ours with just a mound of earth between us. We used to have pitched battles there every lunchtime.

"Bullying went on — as it does in all schools. One trick was for the older boys to get the younger ones to take things out of their desks and then bang the lids down on their knuckles, but I think that's pretty standard.

"Basically, I enjoyed school — especially the social side. I liked messing about at lunchtime.

"I can remember exploring an old factory with a few mates and getting so carried away that we forgot all about the time. Eventually, we were chased out by the owner. Back at school, we were hauled up in front of our housemaster who gave us four of the best across the bum. It was always the same. He used to give us a choice. 'Take your punishment like a man or shall we tell your parents?' We always chose the strap. We knew we'd get far worse at home.

"Another time which ended in the strap was after a lesson with a student teacher. He wasn't much older than us and we were giving him a hard time playing harmonicas and moving furniture around. You know the sort of thing, we thought we were being clever. Suddenly, out of the cupboard, came the most feared teacher of the school — we called him the Loch Ness Monster because he was Scottish. Once again we got four of the best!

"But I wasn't always in trouble or getting the strap — although I wasn't always working, either.

"I was what is known as a gifted child. I was fairly good at everything. I still am, of course," he laughs. "But it's only because I've got a very good memory and that's how I always managed to pass my exams. I never got good grades because I never worked. But I always just scraped through. Some schools would have made me work, and I'd have ended up with ten O-levels and five A-levels, but I'm still glad I went there. I think it was

'The punishment always put me off'

the best thing that ever happened to me. I met all kinds of people and although I didn't leave with many qualifications, I've collected a few more since — basically because I needed them to get a job — boring though that is."

Phil did, in fact, leave with five O-levels — and one A-level in economics, his favourite subject along with engineering. He took a job as a trainee quantity surveyor and specialised, funnily enough, in

'It was the best thing that ever happened to me'

assessing schools for local grants.

At the same time, he began to write the odd joke for comedians like Les Dawson and decided that he'd like to try his hand at full-time script writing. Phil's big break came when he was commissioned to write a comedy script for London Weekend Television. From then on, he never looked back.

Whatever Phil's schooling did or didn't do for him — it gave him a great basis for a series which, as we all know, is as near to the real thing as any programme could be. Like his punishment with the strap — it's one of the best!

Have you never really understood your rights at school?

WELL, NOW YOU KNOW!

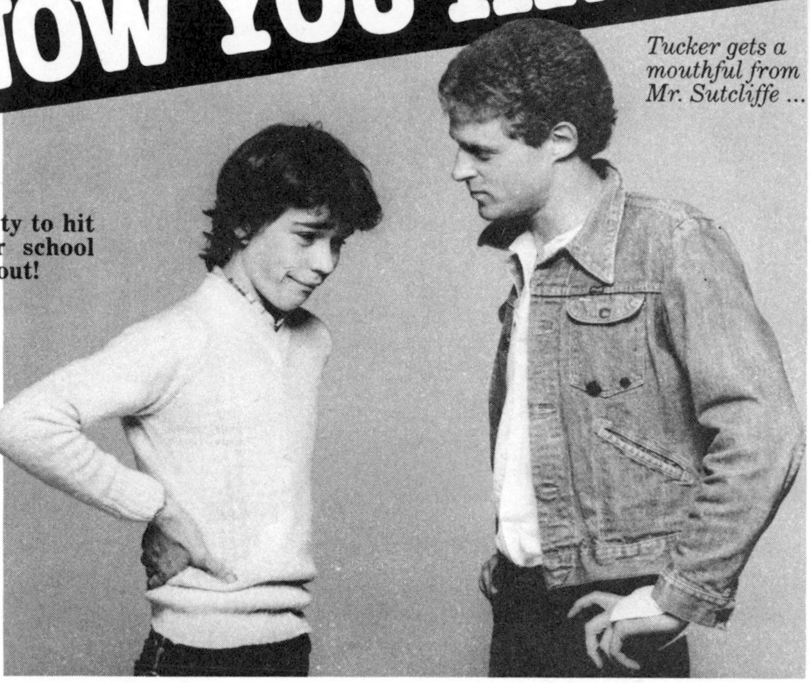

Tucker gets a mouthful from Mr. Sutcliffe ...

DO your teachers have the authority to hit you? Can they make you wear school uniform? This is your chance to find out!

How come we get homework?
Homework is set so that pupils get a better overall view of the subjects they are studying. Homework may be background reading, an essay or an exercise to check that you've understood a previous lesson.

Planning your homework helps you to learn self-discipline. You soon find out it's a mistake to leave things until the last minute.

Most secondary schools and some junior schools set homework.

What happens if I'm expelled?
To be expelled, you must have done something seriously wrong. If you and your mum and dad don't think you have, they can complain to the school governors or the Department of Education.

Anyone under 16 who is expelled from a state school must have their education continued in some way. This may mean a transfer to another school or the provision of a home tutor.

Do I have to stay for detention?
Providing that punishment is 'reasonable,' a teacher can decide how you should be reprimanded for something.

Detentions must be supervised by an adult and extra traffic hazards for children kept in late must be taken into account.

Can a teacher hit me?
Rules about corporal punishment differ from area to area. Some schools use the cane — others a strap. Schools are meant to keep a record of physical punishment. If a teacher is too heavy-handed and causes you physical harm, he/she can be prosecuted.

In London, there are special rules about teachers hitting pupils. These say that boys can be hit on the arm or hand by a teacher's hand — and on the hand or behind by a cane. A girl can only be caned on the hand and cannot be hit by a man at all.

A woman can't hit a boy with her hand, but she can cane him. Punishment must be given in private.

Check your local rules.

What's 'being suspended'?
This means that you are temporarily banned from your school. Only the Head can suspend you and you should be told how long you are suspended for. Some schools send pupils home for up to three days to 'cool off,' but a suspension can be quite a lengthy time. During this period, your education must continue.

Must I wear school uniform?
If your Local Education Authority, the school governors and the Head all agree that uniform must be worn at school, then you have no choice. If they also say it must be worn on the journey to and from school, then you have to comply with that rule, too.

Rules on uniform can forbid you to wear jewellery and boys may be refused permission to grow beards.

Your parents can apply to the LEA for a grant to help with the cost of uniform if they need financial assistance.

Can I get a travel pass?
You qualify for free transport if you are under eight and your school is more than two miles away. Over-eights must live more than three miles from school. However, the LEA can refuse to pay for your fare if there is a suitable school nearer to your home.

Information taken from 'First Rights' issued by the National Council for Civil Liberties and a pamphlet provided by the Hackney Legal Action Group.

What happens if I'm caught playing truant?
Your parents are responsible for making sure that you attend a school once you have been enrolled there. They can be fined up to £200 for failing to do this.

ANSWERS TO QUIZ ON PAGE 27.

	A	B	C
1	10	5	0
2	0	5	10
3	10	5	0
4	0	10	5
5	10	5	0
6	10	5	0
7	5	10	0
8	0	5	10

0-20: Blimey, with friends like yours, who needs enemies?! All they do is get you into trouble and then leave you to face the consequences! The sooner you dump those so-called mates, the better off you'll be!

25-55: Looks like you've got a pretty good group of friends there! They'll stick by you when you're in trouble — but they'll try to steer you clear of it when they can! They're the kind of friends you can have a good laugh with — and that's the best sort to have!

60-80: Watch out next time any of your friends go near a phone box — there's a chance they'll turn into a Supermate! Seriously, though, either you haven't been telling the truth — or your mates are too good to be true!

A LUCKY BREAK!
A Grange Hill Story
A sudden drop in temperature had brought snow to the area . . . and to two Brookdale first years!
WAAAAY! DOWN WITH BROOKDALE!
SPLAT!!
HAVE A CHRISTMAS PRESENT FROM GRANGE HILL!
UH-OH! LOOK OUT, AL! THEY'VE GOT REINFORCEMENTS!
SCARPER!
UP BROOKDALE! GET THEM!
SKID

HEY, COME ON, YOU TWO! IT'S US AGAINST THE BROOKIES!
WHAT ARE YOU ON ABOUT, JENKINS?
LEAVE ME OUT OF YOUR SILLY GAMES!
SUIT YOURSELF! COME ON, AL!
WHAP!!
THEY'RE FROM GRANGE HILL! GETTEM!
AAAGH! LAY OFF!
HEH! HEH! SERVES 'EM RIGHT!
Back at school . . .
THINK OUR GAME'LL BE OFF ON SATURDAY, SIR?
LOOKS PRETTY LIKELY, DOESN'T IT – UNLESS THERE'S A SUDDEN THAW!
STILL, YOU CAN ALWAYS GO ALONG TO THE SPURS IN THE AFTERNOON AND PICK UP A FEW TIPS!
WHAT, AT THEIR PRICES? YOU MUST BE JOKING!
In the cloakroom . . .
WHAT ARE YOU GIRLS DOING IN HERE?
READING, SIR!
OUTSIDE! YOU KNOW THE RULES!
AW, SIR! IT'S FREEZING OUT THERE!

NONSENSE! A SPOT OF FRESH AIR NEVER DID ANYONE ANY HARM!
HUH! TRY TELLING THAT TO THE STAFF UP THERE IN THEIR WARM ROOM!
HEY!
WHAP!!
WAS THAT YOU, DOYLE?
WHAT IF IT WAS? IT WAS AN ACCIDENT!
SOME ACCIDENT! LET'S SEE HOW YOU LIKE IT!
OOH, DOYLEY! YOU'VE HAD IT NOW!
HAVE A TASTE OF YOUR OWN MEDICINE!
OW! OOOH! YOU'RE REALLY HURTING ME!
DOYLEY BEING A PEST, IS HE? WE'LL SHOW YOU HOW IT'S DONE!
LEAVE ME ALONE, JENKINS! I HAVEN'T DONE NOTHING TO YOU!

WELL, THIS IS FOR THE NEXT TIME YOU DO!
THUD!!
BLIMEY! TRUST YOU, TUCKER!
YAAH! MISSED, JENKINS!
WHO THREW THAT SNOWBALL? YOU, HUMPHRIES?
NO, SIR!
IT WAS ME, SIR!
JENKINS! I MIGHT HAVE KNOWN!
YOU KNOW THE FUSS WE'VE HAD THIS YEAR ABOUT BROKEN WINDOWS AND THE COST OF REPLACING THEM . . .
YES, SIR! SORRY, SIR!

SAYING SORRY'S NOT ENOUGH! YOU'LL WRITE OUT A HUNDRED TIMES "I MUST NOT THROW SNOWBALLS NEAR SCHOOL WINDOWS"!
BUT, SIR . . .
AND THAT GOES FOR THE REST OF YOU, TOO! IF I SEE ANYONE THROWING SNOWBALLS, THERE'LL BE TROUBLE!
RRRINGGG!!
ONE AT A TIME! I KNOW YOU'RE ALL KEEN TO GET BACK TO YOUR LESSONS!
I'LL WIPE THAT SMILE OFF DOYLEY'S STUPID FACE!
COME ON, YOU TWO! ALWAYS THE LAST ONES IN!
HOPE YOU ENJOY DOING THOSE LINES, JENKINS!
DON'T KNOW WHAT YOU'RE LOOKING SO PLEASED ABOUT, DOYLE . . .
. . . 'COS I STILL OWE YOU ONE SNOWBALL!
AAAAGH! WATCH IT, JENKINS!
WOULD SOMEONE TELL ME WHAT ALL THE RUMPUS IS ABOUT?
IT'S JENKINS, MISS! HE SHOVED SNOW DOWN MY NECK!
WHEN ARE YOU GOING TO GROW UP, PETER? . . . NOW SETTLE DOWN, EVERYONE!
I'LL GET YOU FOR THAT!

ALL RIGHT, WHO'S NOT HERE TODAY?
LUCY JONES, MISS!
SEE YOU IN THE PLAY-GROUND AT BREAK THEN!
JENKINS! WHY ARE YOU STILL TALKING?
SORRY, MISS!
SAYING SORRY ISN'T ENOUGH! YOU'LL WRITE ME A HUNDRED LINES – "I MUST NOT TALK IN CLASS".
WHAT! BUT, MISS . . . IT WAS DOYLE WHO STARTED IT!
HER AND SOOTY SOUND LIKE A PAIR OF PARROTS! "SAYING SORRY ISN'T ENOUGH!"
IT'S ALL RIGHT FOR YOU TO LAUGH. I'VE GOT TWO HUNDRED LINES TO DO . . . EVEN BEFORE THE FIRST LESSON!
That break-time . . .
WHAT A MORNING! A FLAMING DETENTION NOW!
WELL, YOU WERE COPYING! . . . HEY, WHAT'S GOING ON OVER THERE?
AW!
SPOIL-SPORT!
TRUST TOM-TOM TO SPOIL OUR FUN!
WHAT DOES HE WANNA GO AND SAND OUR SLIDE FOR?
BOILER
NOTHING BETTER TO DO THAN TO SPOIL OTHER PEOPLE'S FUN, I SUPPOSE!
YEAH, TYPICAL!

HEY, I'VE GOT AN IDEA! GIMME A HAND, AL!
DOING WHAT?
Alan soon found out . . .
THIS WAY WITH IT!
YOU ROTTEN PIG, JENKINS! I KNOW WHAT YOU'RE UP TO!
OVER HERE WITH THAT ONE! . . . AND YOURS!
THOMSON'LL DO HIS NUT!
BOILER HOUSE
Soon . . .
RRRINGG!!
HE'LL HAVE A JOB DOING ANY SANDING NOW!
BOILER HOUSE
HOI! WHAT'S GOING ON? . . . BLOOMING KIDS!
HURRY UP, DOYLE! WHERE HAVE YOU BEEN?
TOILET, SIR!

THE HEAD WOULD LIKE TO SEE PETER JENKINS, SIR!
JENKINS? . . . WHAT HAVE YOU BEEN UP TO?
WHAT-EVER IT IS, IT GUARANTEES US TEN MINUTES' PEACE!
That lunch-time . . .
WELL, WHAT DID HE WANT TO SEE YOU ABOUT?
GOT THE BLAME FOR THE SNOW OUTSIDE THE BOILER ROOM, DIDN'T I!
WELL, IT WAS YOUR IDEA, WASN'T IT!
YEAH, OKAY, BUT TOM-TOM DIDN'T KNOW THAT!
SO SOMEONE MUST HAVE TOLD HIM — AND I BETCHA I KNOW WHO!
DOYLE!
AAH, JENKINS! WE'VE BEEN LOOKING FOR YOU!

YOU AND HUMPHRIES! WE'VE GOT A BONE TO PICK WITH YOU AFTER THIS MORNING!
UH? WHAT'RE YOU ON ABOUT, BENNETT?
I'M ON ABOUT A SLIGHT PELTING THAT WE GOT BECAUSE OF YOU!
AND WHICH YOU'RE ABOUT TO GET BACK!
WHAP!!
THUD
HEY! LEAVE OFF!
AAGH!
JUST YOU WAIT, BENNETT!
CAN'T TAKE IT, CAN YOU, JENKINS!
Suddenly . . .
AAAAGH!
CRACK!!
OOOWWW! MY ARM! FEELS LIKE I'VE BUST IT!
YOU ALL RIGHT, TUCKER?

OOOWW! AAAGH!
WHAT'S HAPPENED?
IT'S TUCKER, SIR! HE'S HURT HIMSELF!
AAAH! I CAN'T MOVE IT, SIR!
BETTER GET YOU TO HOSPITAL FOR AN X-RAY! SOMEONE TELL MR. KEATING WHERE WE'VE GONE!
So, next day . . .
NO JENKINS THIS MORNING?
HE'S IN THE TOILET, MISS!
WELL, HE'D BETTER HURRY UP IF HE DOESN'T WANT MORE LINES!
DON'T THINK HE'LL MANAGE ANY MORE, MISS!
SORRY, I'M LATE, MISS!
HAVE TROUBLE WITH YOUR ZIP, JENKINS?
HA, HA!
COULDN'T MANAGE TO DO YOUR LINES OR YOUR HOMEWORK! IT'S MY WRITING ARM!
SKIVER!
I'VE GOT BENNETT TO THANK FOR THIS LUCKY BREAK! I'LL DO THE SAME FOR HIM SOME DAY!
THE END